Julia Fitzgerald has fields. She is the au novels under the na Hamilton and Jane de Vere. She has had several bestsellers in England, and many of her books have been published in the United States, French Canada, France, Germany, Sweden, Norway and Switzerland. In 1984 she became the first British author to receive the Romantic Times Award for Historical Romance and in 1988 she won the Romantic Times Reviewers Choice Award for the Most Exotic Book for her novel, Taboo.

Brought up in the Yorkshire Moors of England, Julia Fitzgerald began writing short stories when she was six years old. Her passion for history, set in the context of the wild beauty of the countryside, first showed itself in hours and hours of her childhood spent drawing queens and princesses in historical costume.

Julia has a diploma in nutrition, and has spent twenty years researching health and astrology. She lectures on both regularly. She was selected by the *Daily Mail* to draw up and compare the birth charts of the Duke and Duchess of York, for the paper's Royal Marriage Souvenir Supplement.

HEALTHY SIGNS

An astrological guide to
health and wellbeing

Julia Fitzgerald

ARROW BOOKS

Arrow Books Limited
62–65 Chandos Place, London WC2N 4NW

An imprint of Century Hutchinson Limited

London Melbourne Sydney Auckland
Johannesburg and agencies throughout
the world

First published 1989
© Julia Fitzgerald 1989

Phototypeset by Input Typsetting Ltd, London
Printed and bound in Great Britain by
Anchor Press Limited, Tiptree, Essex

ISBN 0 09 958980 X

Healthy Signs is dedicated to all the readers of this book, wishing you all good health and happiness

We all return; it is this certainty that gives meaning to life and it does not make the slightest difference whether or not in a later incarnation we remember the former life. What counts is not the individual and his comfort, but the great aspiration to the perfect and the pure which goes on in each incarnation. *Gustav Mahler*, 1860–1911

Whatsoever a man soweth, that shall he also reap. *St Paul*

Perhaps I lived before
In some strange world where first my soul was shaped,
And all this passionate love, and joy, and pain,
That come, I know not whence, and sway my deeds,
Are old imperious memories, blind yet strong,
That this world stirs within me. . . .
       George Eliot, 'The Spanish Gypsy'

Towards the end of a long life, filled with reading, thinking, searching for its explanation, I have yet to find a solution that solves its problems better than the explanation of reincarnation. No saner solution, covering all the facts, presents itself . . . Souls without a past behind them, springing suddenly into existence, out of nothing, with marked mental and moral peculiarities are a conception as monstrous as would be the corresponding conception of babies appearing suddenly from nowhere, unrelated to anybody, but showing marked racial and family types. *Algernon Blackwood*, 'On Reincarnation'

Contents

Introduction

In this book, I hope to introduce readers to the pleasures and benefits of taking their health care into their own hands. Obviously this is not always possible, and not everyone will wish to do so, but I have written *Healthy Signs* for those who want to discover the way to a healthier, happier life.

People think carefully before they put fuel in their cars. They buy the correct grade for the engine. How many think of what they are putting into their mouths? How many know what their bodies' needs are? It is not enough to state that a balanced diet will meet all our requirements. The body (and mind) have different requirements at different times. We need to eat many different foods every day to meet our nutritional needs – foods that should be fresh, grown in rich, healthy soil, then protected from heat, dust and fumes until we purchase them. In an ideal world, we would have no problems; but this is not an ideal world. We reach for brightly coloured, sweet-tasting foods, but the artificial, man-made products do us no good at all. For decades now we have been seduced by refined foods, and I can speak from experience when I say that it is not always easy to discard these. As a child, I was a sugar addict. The first step is to eat a healthy diet, rich in unadulterated proteins, a large proportion of which will be of vegetable origin. Include plenty of fresh vegetables, fruits, wholegrains and complex, unrefined carbohydrates, and gradually reduce the number of stimulants you eat and drink. There is more information on these lines to help you as you read through this book.

On the astrology side, there is more awareness of the physical rulership of some signs than others. For instance, Scorpio's association with the sexual organs has particularly captured people's imaginations. Not only the sun sign rulership is important where astrological vulnerabilities (and strengths) are concerned, however. The ascendant or rising sign (that is, the sign of the zodiac rising on the eastern horizon at the moment an infant takes its first breath) is also involved, as is the moon, and any signs which feature strongly in the birthchart (e.g. what is called a satellitium, or stellium, of planets, which means three or more planets in one sign). Planets in the sixth house, the house of health, also influence matters. Those who have Neptune in, or ruling, the sixth are especially vulnerable where drugs and strong medicines are concerned, as are those with a Piscean sun or moon sign, Neptune on the ascendant or conjunct the sun sign. Where possible, natural remedies should always be sought from birth for Neptune-ruled subjects.

A particular sign does not always endow a susceptibility in the bodily area that it governs. Frequently there may be extra strength, beauty, talent or skill instead. For example, the sign Gemini, rules the lungs, and there may be a superb and powerful singing voice, as with Judy Garland and Alison Moyet. Astrology has always brought more good news than bad. However, it is always wise to be aware in advance of where weaknesses might lie, so that preventative measures can be taken.

Those who know only their sun signs can consult that section and also the other sections ruled by the same element. If Earth-ruled Taurus, for instance, then also read the Virgo and Capricorn sections.

For those born on what is called the cusp, that is, between the seventeenth and twenty-fifth of each month, it may be helpful to read the section for the sign before or after yours. For example, is your birthday is on 19 September, then read the Virgo section and the Libra section. If it is on 20 October, then read both the Libra and Scorpio sections.

The signs come in triplicities. Three are ruled by Fire (Aries, Leo and Sagittarius); three are ruled by Earth (Taurus, Virgo and Capricorn); three are ruled by Air (Gemini, Libra and Aquarius); and three are ruled by Water (Cancer, Scorpio and Pisces.) Some common characteristics are shared by signs in each of the triplicities.

Should you know only your sun sign, but have a particular health problem, then read the section that provides information on that area of the body. Sign rulerships are as follows:

ARIES: The head and brain
TAURUS: The throat, throat area and thyroid
GEMINI: The lungs, nervous system, arms, hands, shoulders
CANCER: The stomach and breasts
LEO: The heart, heart area, spine
VIRGO: The abdomen, intestines
LIBRA: The kidneys and renal system, lower part of the back
SCORPIO: The sexual organs, prostate, anal area, pelvis
SAGITTARIUS: The hips and thighs, liver
CAPRICORN: The knees, skeleton, teeth and skin
AQUARIUS: The circulatory system, ankles, shins
PISCES: The feet, lymph system, pituitary, duodenum

As so many problems can be averted in childhood, I include a section on the child of each sign, in the hope that parents or guardians, and teachers, will read, digest and put into practice. There are mothers who cannot resist their adorable babies and feed them sweets and processed foods because the babies crave them. Childhood cravings inevitably lead to adult health problems of one kind or another. If you want your children to live long and healthily, without enduring illness or a frail and painful old age, then feed them a nourishing, natural diet which includes as little white sugar and refined foods as possible. I generally agree with the maxim 'You are what you eat', but in the case of refined white sugar, the eater does not become more refined! They become tired, moody and susceptible to infection. In some cases, refined sugar can even stoke up violence and aggression. It affects the metabolism and dulls the mind.

We are extremely fortunate today to have so many therapies available to us. We do not have to suffer in silence. Now we have all the benefits of Eastern medicine on hand, too: herbs and acupuncture from China, yoga and Ayurvedic medicine from India. From England we have the Bach flower remedies; from Austria, homeopathy; and a wealth of dietary advice and information from both East and West. Aromatherapy was extensively developed by the Egyptians, who were skilled in the use of precious oils and essences, along with such resins and gums as frankincense and myrrh of Biblical fame. Every time we smell a flower, or put on scent, we are practising aromatherapy of a kind.

The Bach flower remedies were created by Dr Edward Bach, a man who was totally in tune with Nature in a way that few people are today. Although the remedies are not associated with particular zodiac signs – despite the name 'the Twelve Healers' given to the twelve original remedies, this does not have any astrological connection – I am recommending them here. They could not be more simple to select, and it was Dr Bach's wish that their prescribing should not be complicated by any theories or systems. For example, if you are irritable or angry, you choose impatiens. If you are beset by gloom and depression, you choose mustard.

Please read the Bach booklets before making your selection, or consult the Centre if you have any queries. The flower remedies are completely harmless. There are more details about them and Dr Bach in the index of this book.

Whenever an ethnic group alters its traditional diet to that of the West, as, for example, when Oriental people move to America and eat Western junk foods, they invariably develop the health problems of their new culture. The original Greek diet was close to perfection: fish, olive oil, garlic, fresh vegetables and a salad with every meal, roughly milled bread. . . . The older generations of Cretan males actually drink olive oil daily for the vigour it gives them. Now, after some years on Western junk foods – sugary canned drinks, flour bright and white for the tourists, chips, ice creams, sweets, more cooked dishes and meat every day – the Greeks are suffering increasing heart disease. The Western way of eating is tremendously seductive, associated with affluence and success as it is. Unfortunately, refined sugars and grains, additives, artificial colourings, sugary drinks, tea and coffee and sugar-cured tobacco find little success with the human body.

Now it is faulty diet that decimates people, not war. The price for affluence is all too often disease and early death.

Unfortunately, with a very few exceptions, the National Health Service has not interested itself in diet and vitamin therapy. In 1987, the BMA denounced alternative remedies such as herbalism. NHS now stands for No Healthy Solution, for when minds are closed in this way, they are closed to the truth. It is not enough to say that a herb or home-opathic remedy is ineffectual because it has not been clinically tested, or that acupuncture does not work because it cannot be proven. What has served the Chinese well for thousands of years cannot be dismissed so arrogantly. Homeopathy works equally well on animals, who most certainly are not responding to any psychological persuasion! My cats are all treated with homeopathic remedies when necessary, with excellent results. There are no side effects, and the body does not react as if assaulted, as it does with many drugs. Doctors are not given any training in nutrition, so they cannot pronounce on this subject – and yet they do, continually. Only a few years ago, they were insisting that white bread was as nourishing and healthy as wholemeal and that exercise wouldn't help anyone to slim! Alternative practitioners have been recommending wholegrains for many decades. Read the books by Gaylord Hauser, who has been advocating wholegrains since 1922!

However modern and civilised we think we are, we are still Mother Nature's children and we need to return to the old natural ways. Children should respect their Mother, not neglect and ignore Her. In return, She will protect and care for us a hundred-fold. We are born of the Earth and She is born of us. We live – or we die – as one.

1

ARIES

Astrology represents the summation of all the psychological knowledge of antiquity. *Carl Jung*

Astrology is a way to understand people and see the heaven that is in them.
Rod Chase, American astrologer

Aries the Ram: c. 21 March–c. 21 April   Element: Fire. Planetary ruler: Mars. Physical rulership: the head, brain, eyes, upper part of the jaw. By polarity with Libra: the kidneys and lumbar area of spine.

Destiny of Aries: to break new ground without stealing others' limelight and without arguing. To forget self.

Herbs for Aries: garlic, onions, all-heal, marsh rose-mary, horseradish, sweet marjoram, shepherd's rod, sarsaparilla, nettle, cowslip. Because Ariens take risks and do everything with such vigour, they may break more than one bone in their lifetime and comfrey (knitbone is its old country name) will be useful at these times.

Gems for Aries: ruby and jasper, garnet. In the Middle Ages the ruby was used as a guardian against plague, despair and evil, being considered a health protector and cheer-bringer. To Christians the jasper is the symbol of faith and red is the colour of martyrdom. Mary Queen of Scots wore red at her execution and so did Anne Boleyn, second wife of Henry VIII.

Vital vitamins and minerals for Aries: vitamin C, to keep

the red blood cells vital. Vitamin E, to keep the red blood cells vigorous, to speed wound healing and the prevention of scars. B complex for skin rashes, mouth lesions, sore or inflamed tongue, blood deficiencies. Iron and folic acid for strong blood. Phosphorus for the brain. See Libra for protective regime for kidneys.

The myth behind the motivation

Aries heads the zodiac. It is the first sign, the starter, the innovator, and the head is that part of the body ruled by Aries. The red blood cells, too, come under its jurisdiction. Impulsive, headstrong and determined, Ariens brook no interference when involved in one of their crusades or missions. The world owes a great deal to their zeal, their pioneering spirit, their gift for brilliant invention and ingenious turn of thought. All the same, this dynamism can be somewhat difficult to handle in the home. They are restless, active people, needing only a few hours' sleep and so determined to get what they want that others can be trampled in the process. It is wonderful to be loved by an Arien and agony to be forgotten by them as they sweep onwards to another conquest. Highly sexed, they can fritter away their passions with an endless stream of affairs, as did Casanova, or ruin their reputations by letting their desires get the upper hand, as did Rasputin.

They make life colourful – and sometimes very difficult – for others, but their ability to get the ball rolling, their genius for instigating matters, is a vital talent that we could not manage without. The world would be a bland and old-fashioned place without them, even though at times we might curse them for their exuberance and overbearing temperament. That rebellious edge that steers them can be enormously valuable in shaking the stick-in-the-mud foundations of society when needed – but at its worst it can be the reckless fire of the terrorist, the guerilla and the mercenary.

As they bound around, bursting with enthusiasm, it's hard to imagine Ariens having to endure any complaint, but even the hardiest sometimes suffer from headaches and accidents to the head. (There is always a price for being first!) Thick-skinned, they can be infamous for their apparent insensitivity, yet they are loyal and staunch friends and can be depended upon in any crisis. The females of the sign have abundant energy for their own families and frequently foster or adopt children. Their hearts are large, yet some can be sharp-tongued and overstrict, and the fiery Aries temper is the sort that makes people run for cover. It rarely lasts, though, and there are no sulks afterwards.

Mars, their ruling planet, is indefatigable, direct, guileless, forthright, independent and able to overcome all barriers. Hot-headed at worst, it ploughs through all objections, all defences. Leading sportsmen frequently have Mars in a prominent position in their birthcharts. Only from Roman times have we seen Mars as the bringer of war, for prior to that he was a harvest god, the sacrificial victim when the corn was reaped, his death the assurance of a successful crop in the year to follow. As the Earth Goddess's mate, his was only a supportive role, at the end of which he volunteered to die. This is a very different image from that of the modern Arien, who will brook no secondary role, and yet the altruism is still there when needed.

The Aries epoch of Ram worship was c. 1953 BC – c. 220 AD, following after the great age of Taurus and Bull worship. Women had enjoyed a prominent role

in the Taurean age as the high priestesses of the
Great Goddess, Mother Earth, in all her manifes-
tations: Isis, Ishtar, Inanna, Hathor, to list but four
of her names. (Queen Jezebel, condemned for all
time as a woman of the foulest evil, refused to
abandon her worship of the Great Goddess; that was
her supposed 'crime'.) When the Arien age swept
in on a tide of war and gradually growing Roman
dominance, it became a case of 'We are right; do as
we say, or else!' Roman soldiers wore ram's horns
on their uniforms. They worshipped Pallas Athena,
who wore armour and ram's horns on her helmet.
(She was born from her father's head, fully armed –
all symbolic of Aries.) The massive carved battering
ram ensured the fall of many a besieged city and
township, and the Roman legions took live rams with
them on their campaigns. The Roman energy,
impulse, motivation and martial ability were all Arien
in origin. So was the fiery burning bush of Moses,
and Jehovah's insistence that He must be worshipped alone, and that there are no other gods but
Him. There was to be no chance of humankind
returning to the worship of the Great Goddess: the
laws forbidding women any kind of power, repu-
tation in her own right or independence were built
into the new, male-dominated religion by the Indo-
European invaders, then the Hebrews and Muslims,
but most substantially by the Christians. The
Hebrews smashed and desecrated all shrines to the
Goddess, murdering anyone who stood in their way,
'by order' of their male god. This is Aries/Mars at
his worst and most aggressive, but the effects have
continued because of the insistence during the past
two thousand years on male-orientated religion.

'They came, they saw, they conquered', could well
have been penned as an Arien motto.

In ancient times, the New Year began on 15 March,

under Mars, and when January was adopted in its place, some of the customs of March were moved along with it, such as the decorating of houses with greenery. The priests of Mars wore military-style robes for their spring ceremonies and carried spears which were believed to embody the god. March was the month when battles were resumed after the hiatus caused by winter weather. These Martian priests were equally involved in the resumption of agricultural growth after winter, for their god was the protector of the growing grain and ploughland. Horse races were run and a horse sacrificed to Mars, as were unborn calves on 21 April, the Arien birthday of Rome itself.

If Ariens could revive some of that ancient connection with the Earth and take time out to care for and appreciate Nature, they would find it a very healing process. It would be better still if they could turn their crusading zeal to ecological welfare.

Not surprisingly, accidents feature in Arien lives, frequently caused by their impulsive behaviour and their craving for the speed and danger that excites them. They may suffer head-on crashes, driving accidents, burns (Aries is a fire sign, and fire needs careful handling) or falls out of trees, for they love to tackle supposedly impossible feats with that fierce, burning energy that will brook no interference. 'Stop' is a word unknown to them. For them, the red light is a green light. They can be impatient, reckless drivers, foolhardy and prepared to take silly risks, convinced of their ability to survive.

The gutsy courage of Mars is behind the Princess Royal's readiness to get up bravely after falling off her horse in front of so many critical eyes. It is also why she tries and tries again at such a demanding sport, and why she works tirelessly in support of the Save the Children Fund.

Mars conjunct Margaret Thatcher's sun sign gives her that vital energy, too, and the need for only a few hours' sleep each night. She is the only Prime Minister who has not aged drastically while in power. Ariens are long-lived, and Mars in a powerful position can bring longevity – it also increases the likelihood of accidents, so care must be taken when travelling.

The Duchess of York also has Mars conjunct her sun sign, which is why she was able to get up at six every morning and continue her publishing career while enjoying her new marriage and carrying out public engagements with such verve.

Many great conductors are Ariens or Mars-ruled, and long-lived with it. This is the secret behind their advanced ages, and not the fact that they exercise their arms vigorously, as someone has suggested! Notice how conductors move their heads in time to the music. . . .

It has been said that Ariens have the attention span of a toddler, and it is true that they can be petulant, greedy, ruthless, explosive and turbulent; but this is also the sign of the genius and the inventor. Some of our greatest artists have been Ariens: Van Dyck, Goya, Van Gogh, Raphael, Leonardo de Vinci, William Morris, Holman Hunt, Lalique, Rousseau, Madame Vigée-Lebrun and Fragonard. Remember that one is said to have an eye for painting, and that the eye is, of course, Aries-ruled.

When that high-voltage energy overpowers them, Ariens can suffer, as Van Gogh did, and then they need rest and peace, quiet country walks and the company of the animals they love to put them back on an even keel. They adore dogs, often finding cats a little too peaceful for their tastes. Although bright red is their planetary colour, it is very inflammatory, and this is one sign that never needs inflaming!

Soothing blue is restorative to them and it is wise to keep something of this colour in the place where they are most likely to blow their tops, so that they can look at it and absorb its calming vibrations. A blue office or workshop is always a good idea for Ariens. Bracing walks in the peace of the countryside, taking an interest in Nature and all its glories, sensible eating – and eating slowly, chewing their food and not bolting it – can return them to their former good spirits. Remember that they were once harvest gods, glorying in their vital role in Mother Nature's plan, and that a return to Nature can restore their equilibrium even though they may treasure the bright city lights that burn all night.

Fortunately, their powers of recovery are strong, and nothing keeps them down for long; but if they believe that they are invincible, then something may well come along to prove to them that they are only human after all – and then a sacrifice might be necessary. It is better for them to be willing than to be driven.

Ariens are often positive that they do not have time or patience for restorative techniques such as meditation and yoga and deep breathing, but these can bring them untold benefits. Instead of stretching themselves so tautly that they snap and snarl, they can achieve more with less effort and stay calmer – and make fewer enemies in the process. Autohypnosis is often the answer, for it can be learned quickly and just a few deep breaths can bring the required relaxation. Getting past the tension barrier is one of the problems, for they love an adrenalin high, but autohypnosis overcomes this and it bears many fruits. Ideas flow faster and brighter; energy levels do not fluctuate so much; headaches are kept at bay; sleep is deeper; troublesome excess tension is relaxed away.

In ancient Egypt, Amun, the ram-headed god, the first of the gods to be created, was worshipped by his fellow gods. He was accustomed to having premier place, to giving his views freely and to having them taken seriously. Those curly horns that can look so ferocious in battle can give their subjects eyebrows that frown or curve down to the nose and wing their way high up onto the forehead. (Authors Jeffrey Archer and James Herbert and actor Steve McQueen are three excellent examples.) Ariens have pale to medium blue eyes and fair hair that is sometimes bright gold, are small to medium-boned and of small to medium build. Tending to jut their heads forward as they walk, they often have very wide smiles and show a lot of teeth. Aries rules Germany, where the Aryan ideal of a fair-haired, blue-eyed race was formulated. Unfortunately, the Ariens' belief in their own omnipotence and infallibility had unhappy consequences for Germany, as it also did for Aries-ruled Japan.

This is one sign that never has a weight problem. They fidget a lot, moving about, often moving their heads jerkily. Sporty, they may prefer unisex clothes, tracksuits and trainers, but they can also be bandbox neat and smart, and love to focus attention on their heads by wearing ornate and decorative hats. (Barbara Cartland is Aries rising. It is her Cancerian sun sign that makes her dress so romantically, for Ariens usually decline to wear frills and ornamentation.) They may appear impatient when listening to others talk, being barely able to control their response. At their worst, they are pushy, argumentative, domineering and ruthless. At their best, they are loyal, tireless friends, working indefatigably for worthy causes. (Anna Sewell, author of *Black Beauty*, campaigned all her life for better treatment of horses.) Or they may become renowned for writing about war, as with John Jakes and Frederick E. Smith, author of 633 *Squadron*, or about violence itself, as with Robert Bloch, author of *Psycho*. And both captain and second in command of the *Starship Enterprise*, William Shatner and Leonard Nimoy are Ariens. Ariens are made for command.

The Aries child

Arien children are outspoken, restless, tactless creatures who gulp down food, flourish at sport, and think that arguing is a way of life. Tending to have the free-fall parachuter's approach to life, their wild, impetuous attitude can continue if they aren't lovingly disciplined. They must be taught that other people have to be allowed their opposing views. Arien children need plenty to occupy them to keep them out of mischief. Fast food eaten on the run is their delight, so a sensible wholefood diet is essential to prevent bad habits forming. They have special requirements for the B-complex vitamins, iron and calcium (a tranquilliser). This child, who finds sitting still so difficult, might be judged hyperactive at school, when it is simply their enormous abundance of energy that is the cause. Despite this, they may enjoy painting and be gifted at it. They love animals and will care for them devotedly, and music, medicine, science, discoveries, astronomy, and finding out about new worlds, all appeal to them. Any signs of tiredness or headache need quiet and gentle attention, but it is likely to be more of a spiritual weariness than physical. In past times, many Ariens were profoundly religious people – St Teresa of Avila being a prime example – but there is little opportunity for such zealousness now. All the same, the missionary and the crusader can turn their energies to fields other than religion.

That keen, sharp eye must be protected with vitamin C from infancy onwards (the eye requires twenty times more vitamin C than the rest of the body, and the eyes are the first to suffer when it is in short supply) and vitamin A. Foods high in vitamin A or beta-carotene are: red and yellow vegetables such as carrots, dried apricots, liver, beef and chicken liver, fish and fish oils, watercress, spinach, cherries, peaches, broccoli, the dark green outer leaves of vegetables, alfalfa, cheese and butter. Beta-carotene is the precursor of vitamin A, which means that the body can transform it into vitamin A as required. One cannot overdose on beta-carotene. Air pollution, food processing and smoking, or inhaling the smoke from others' cigarettes, use up vitamins A and C at a galloping pace. Vitamin C is destroyed by anything that stresses the body, e.g. caffeine, colds and exposure to infections. Cooking, storage, heat and light affect both these vitamins. Iron and copper cooking vessels also destroy vitamin A. Copper destroys vitamin C. If you have copper or lead water pipes, run off the water each morning before use – especially if you are making drinks for children. Vegetables and fruit should be organically grown, freshly picked and either raw or lightly cooked in just enough water to prevent burning.

Foods high in vitamin C are: acerola cherries, peppers (the redder the better), blackcurrants, rosehips, citrus fruits, guavas, parsley, kale, Brussels sprouts, chives, watercress, cauliflower, strawberries, cabbage, mustard and cress, blackberries and lychees. The potato is often quoted as a good source, but after it has been cut into thin strips and boiled in oil, there isn't much vitamin C left! Jacket potatoes are healthiest. Oranges that have travelled thousands

of miles to reach us may well be low in vitamin C.
Every cigarette smoked uses up 30 mgms of vitamin
C, and children do tend to try out these things in
secret. . . . All exposure to pollution destroys vitamin
C, so there should be plenty in the daily diet in food
and pill form – and it is not advisable to stop using
it suddenly, as enzyme levels drop while it is being
taken and they need a little time to restore
themselves.

Most important is to encourage Arien children to
relax at regular intervals. They may prefer doing this
through sport, but country walking is one of the most
restorative pastimes for Ariens – especially if they are
reluctant to exercise more vigorously. Trips into the
countryside should be on the family agenda from an
early age, with books on flowers and birds and
insects for nature-spotting together and sketch books
and paints, too. If this becomes a familiar way of
spending time for Arien children, they will have
many hours of happy relaxation, and they will thank
their parents for it.

Health

Learning how to relax is one of the most important
lessons any Arien can learn. Resting with the feet up
and cucumber or potato slices on the eyes will prove
restorative, as will splashing closed eyes with cold
water daily to improve circulation. Palming is one of
the Bates eye-healing methods – sitting in a relaxed
position, elbows resting on a table, palms over closed
eyes, heels of palms resting gently on cheekbones.
Ariens should think of the happiest things that have
ever happened to them while relaxing in this black
velvet valley for ten to fifteen minutes. Breathing
deeply and evenly increases the benefits. Stress

restricts the circulation to the brain and eyes, and this is one way of intervening in that vicious circle.

Shepherd's purse is recommended for bloodshot eyes, eye pain and glaucoma, and can be obtained from herbalists. In Chinese medicine, the eye is connected with the liver, and this is supported by Western naturopathy. A body that is stagnating because of a congested and underactive liver will hoard its poisons, and the eyes will suffer as a result. So will the complexion, which will be blotchy and blemished.

Aries is a nervy and highly strung sign, and Ariens need to avoid white sugar, which interferes with the body's nervous system. There are a number of reasons to avoid white sugar: it has only recently been introduced into our diet, and our bodies have developed no defence against it. It robs the bones and teeth of calcium. It disturbs the body's insulin production and creates a sometimes uncontrollable appetite for sugar and yet more sugar. It provides empty calories that fill us with nothing and leave no room for nutrition-rich food. Children are particularly vulnerable to its ill effects. The teeth are part of the skeleton; if sugar is damaging our teeth, what is it doing to the rest of our bones? Think of that before you buy yourself or your child sweets and chocolate. It is no good having the most powerful mind in the world if the body is too weak and badly nourished to support it.

In his eye-opening book *Sugar Blues* William Dufty tells how, in those awful Vietnam war days, he was told by a Japanese philosopher that if America really wanted to conquer the North Vietnamese, then they must drop sweet things on them: sugar, candy and Coca-Cola, as 'that will destroy them faster than bombs'.

Slaves died in their millions so that we could

indulge our ever-increasing sweet tooth by importing sugar and molasses. Now we die in their place because of our high consumption of it. It is a very seductive element (I refuse to call it a food). We always want more; we crave sweet things. There is a very good reason for this. When we eat sugar, we get a temporary 'high', but our body has to pour out insulin to cope with its effects. The excess sugar is removed but the insulin stays high for some time and we crave more sugar. Then we get those famous sugar blues and feel dull, sleepy and drained. Sweets are the handiest foods, neatly packaged, small, portable and – literally – packing a punch. What do they punch? The adrenal glands that strive to protect us from this stressful 'merry'-go-round, and the pancreas that struggles to produce enough insulin to cope with all the refined poison. When it collapses exhausted from the fight, diabetes sets in. Diabetes is now at epidemic proportions, a direct result of our over-indulgence in sugar and sugary foods.

Read labels carefully. Sugar comes in many disguises; glucose, dextrose, syrup and sucrose all have the same effect on the pancreas as white sugar. I once spoke to a worker at a famous sweets company and asked him how he felt about filling children with so much sugar. 'We don't use sugar,' he replied confidently. 'What do you use then?' I asked. 'Sucrose,' he replied, still confident, either not knowing or not caring that sucrose is the chemical name for white sugar.

Ariens should remember that insidious poisonous effect it has and kick sugar out of their diet to keep their eyes sharp and bright, their famed energy on an even keel and the nervous system strong and calm.

High-fibre foods, unpeeled fruits, proteins, oats and oat bran all help to maintain blood-sugar levels

without those ups and downs that affect mood.
There is great confusion about blood sugar and white
sugar, a confusion which has been put to good use
by the sugar industry. Blood sugar is *not* the same as
the sugar in sweets and cakes and puddings. Refined
sugar will give a short spurt of energy, yes, but in
doing so it puts the body under such great stress that
in fact you shorten your days of health. The pancreas
was not created to deal with blood-sugar levels
shooting up and down repeatedly each day. It cannot
cope. Now we have tea and coffee, alcohol, cigarettes
and sugar all stressing the pancreas, and eventually
it has to give up the fight. Take pity on this small
but essential organ, and eat wholefoods, high in fibre
and as nature intended them to be eaten: fresh,
organically grown and unadulterated.

Back to that well-known saying, 'You are what you
eat.' If you doubt this, go and see the film *The Fly*.
When the hero of this salutary tale is changing from
human form into that of a repugnant fly, he craves
sweets and sugar. It is a brilliant performance by Jeff
Goldblum, in which he displays all the nervous, jerky
tension that is the direct result of a high consumption
of refined sugar.

The Bach flower remedies are easily taken without
any inconvenience – which is how Ariens like their
medicines – and they work gently but thoroughly on
mind and spirit. There is a more detailed explanation
of the remedies in the appendix of this book, and it
is advisable to read some of the Bach booklets before
making a final selection, especially where more than
one flower is given. The remedies can work even
where a problem seems insurmountable.

The Arien temperament can be admired and
envied, or feared. If they eat wisely and do not
imagine in their Martian arrogance that they can live
on thin air and junk food and still thrive, then they

should not fall victim to the worst excesses of rage, fury and argumentativeness. Hopefully, they will thereby ensure that the Martian energies are turned towards a good and worthy cause and not against themselves and those they love.

Herbal teas for Aries

Red Zinger. Ruby Red by Floradix. Rosehip by Jill Davies. Any of the relaxing and calming teas, such as Chamomile by the London Herb and Spice Company. Evening Peace by Jill Davies, or Sleep-Tight by San Francisco. Norfolk Punch each night if feeling stressed and overtired. For migraines: feverfew, angelica, lime, rosemary.

2

TAURUS

> The wise man rules his stars, the fool
> obeys them.

Taurus the Bull: c. 22 April–c. 22 May   Element:
Earth. Planetary ruler: Venus. Physical rulership:
throat, thyroid, larynx, tonsils. By polarity with
Scorpio: the sexual organs.

Destiny of Taurus: to love and indulge others without
thought of return. To heed advice sometimes, if not
always.

Herbs for Taurus: garden mint, lovage, colt's foot,
garden or wild thyme, tansy, primrose, strawberries,
plums, peach and pear trees.

Vital vitamins and minerals for Taurus: vitamin C, to
help clear out the excesses of overindulgence.
Vitamin E, to oxygenate the blood and keep the
thyroid gland healthy. Iodine to feed the thyroid.

Gems for Taurus: blue sapphire, lapis lazuli, rose
quartz, nephrite, emerald, pink diamond. Colours:
blue and pink. The Greeks considered the sapphire
the most sacred of stones. To Christians, blue
represents the heavens, the firmament, fidelity,
constancy and integrity. It has a special association
with the Virgin Mary. Green in Christian art is the
symbol of hope and victory, and the colour of spring.

The myth behind the motivation

Cows are considered bovine and uninteresting today, but once they were revered as sacred (as they still are in India, of course). Bull and cow worship dominated the pre-Roman world, when the cow was seen as the benevolent cosmic mother, her milk flowing freely, gladly given to her earthly children, while the bull was seen as embodying the powerful forces of Nature, fertile, vigorous, unconquered. Knossos in Crete was built around the cult of the Bull, at a time when this beast reigned supreme. In ancient Egypt, the Apis bulls were worshipped as Ptah's 'glorious soul'. After their death, they became one with Osiris. (Ptah was the Supreme Creator God of Egypt, Osiris the God of Agriculture and the Realms of the Dead.) The bulls lived a life of indulged luxury, with sacrifices being made to them, until it was time for them to be sacrificed in their turn. This had to be done while they were still fit and strong, because they embodied Nature, and those were the days when climate and harvest meant the difference between life and death. The new bull would be selected rather in the way that the Tibetan Lama still is. It would be chosen because of a particular identifying mark on its body, and then it would reign supreme for its allotted span. Its strength was our strength, and while it flourished, so did the Earth.

Hathor was the Cow Goddess par excellence, a benevolent queen who nurtured and protected her people. The crescent-shaped horns of the cow were her symbol, representing the curving horns of the moon. The Milky Way was her universal nourishment for humanity. Hathor is sometimes depicted as a beautiful woman, as in the enchanting sculptures at her temple in Denderah, or she is represented as a majestic cow with towering horns. There are

paintings of her suckling the infant Pharaohs. The
cow was 'the fruitful image of the all-producing
goddess'.

Taureans are strong and long-lived. They enjoy the
luxurious life – which is one parallel – but they do
not find it easy to make sacrifices, to give up what
they most enjoy, whether it is their favourite food,
wine or pastime. Maybe they are receiving their
rewards now for all that past sacrifice, or it could be
that so many centuries of being worshipped as gods
whittled away their ability to go without. Most likely,
it is something of both.

Taureans have big hearts and will care for children
and animals unstintingly – there is a very strong
bond between a cow and her calf – but they find it
hard to discipline them, so their house might be a
somewhat noisy place, but always happy.

The May Day celebrations that children love are
strongly associated with Taurus, for the May Queen,
clad in green and flower-decked, is the Goddess
returning from the frost-clad grip of winter, when
hardship and rationing are flung aside and plenty
returns. Another reason that the Taurean finds it
difficult to accept rationing or to go without is that
ever-present memory of spring's burgeoning in their
mind. Their love is like that, too – steady, deep and
strong, laden with gifts and offerings, and rarely
unfaithful. To be loved by a member of this sign can
be paradise. They are generous, tactile, bountiful,
affectionate, doting and passionate. If they are sure
of your love then they will show a more adventurous
side to their nature. Their occasional bursts of temper
are most likely to be stirred by jealousy.

Much has been said – most of it derogatory – about
Taureans and their possessive instincts. Even their
partners become their possessions, it is claimed. Yet
surely it is better to be needed by someone who

loves you, cares deeply for you and looks after you
tenderly, than it is to be married to some one who
does not care one iota where you are or who you are
with. If it is loving care and attention that you need,
then go to a Taurean. All they ask in return is a little
appreciation.

Taureans are the guardians, the caretakers. They
collect and acquire, gather and tend. Because of
Taureans (and also some Virgoans), we have
beautiful paintings, magnificent antiques, carpets
and jewellery, precious books and sumptuous
clothes which can be seen and enjoyed in galleries,
museums and stately homes. At its worst such
acquisitiveness may become greedy hoarding, but
what a potential value it has for others!

Steady, dependable and practical, Taureans need
time to adjust to new ideas. They do not like to be
rushed into things – and, in fact, it may be impossible
to hasten them. They like to reflect, to ponder, to
adjust to new possibilities. Some of them are
extremely shy and suffer agonies in public, assuming
a silent manner that suggests coldness or disinterest,
which is very far from being the case. These Taureans
need time to come round to new friends and new
situations, but when they do so, they are wonderful,
loyal lifelong friends. There is none of the changeable
Geminian or the histrionic Leo about these earth-
rooted, solid, warm-hearted people. Some of them
make excellent healers, pouring out that protective,
enveloping warmth onto those in need. That same
warmth ensures that children and plants flourish in
their care, and that friends in need can always go to
them and be assured of help and a comforting word.

Sensual, tactile and passionate, they love silks and
velvets and plush velours. Some of the greatest cour-
tesans have been born under this sign, such as Emma
Hamilton, and women with a prodigious sexual

appetite, such as Catherine the Great. Their beauty
and charm makes it easy for them to be loved, but
they need an equally faithful and responsive mate.
They can be heartbroken by fickle lovers and may
shut themselves away from life as a result. The older
widows and widowers of this sign may be very
cautious about remarrying.

Naturally talented with money and business
matters, they can find themselves wealthy at a
comparatively young age, or studying hard for future
wealth. They are never foolish with money; they
know how to handle it, but although they are careful,
they are rarely mean. If you have met that rare entity,
a mean Taurus, then you will find that discontent
has coloured their whole life. They are not like other
Taureans: their giving qualities have been choked
before they could blossom, and they are deeply
unhappy.

Venus and Earth are their rulers, and some of them
are very Venusian: glamorous, gorgeous to look at,
with thick dark hair or blonde curls, fascinating eyes
that change colour from greens to blues to greys or
greeny blues – the change of colour is the pointer to
Venus's influence. Dimples are another of Venus's
features, along with a curvaceous shape, a small
waist, and generous bosom and hips. They may have
a cowlick on their foreheads or tight little curls there.
Like Librans, they have cupid's bow mouths, snub
noses and soft, gently rounded features. Their eyes
may be almond shaped or deep set. Greta Garbo has
Taurus moon, and a Virgoan sun sign giving her that
cool, sculpted beauty. Joan Collins has her moon in
Taurus (having Gemini sun and ascendant keeps her
enviably slim and zipping with energy). The men do
not always fare so well, and the strong, stocky
Taurean build can soon become fleshiness, yet they
have a natural dignity and handsomeness that tend

to make one ignore the fat. Clark Gable had Taurus
rising: Taurus at its best physically, with charisma,
good looks and a mesmeric smile. They love music
and dancing, and singing is their great talent. Some
of the greatest voices of all time have been Taureans;
for example, Elvis Presley was Taurus rising and with
dark, slumbrous Taurean looks. Others with the
powerful voice of this sign include Cher, Ella Fitzgerald, Dame Nellie Melba, Billy Joel, Barbra Stre-
isand, Bing Crosby, Hazel O'Connor, Stevie Wonder
and Burt Bacharach. Actors with richly smooth
Taurean voices include James Mason, Orson Welles,
Glenda Jackson, Stewart Granger and Laurence
Olivier (Gemini–Taurus cusp). David Jacobs, the
radio and television presenter, also has the
mellifluous Venusian voice, and reclusive Irving
Berlin was born under this sign. Unlike Ariens, who
rattle out their words and are never short of something to say, Taureans reflect before they speak,
liking to mull over their words first. Sometimes they
do this to such an extent that people may mistakenly
think they are slow-witted. A Taurean can never be
rushed, verbally or physically.

The Earthy Taureans, like the Queen, enjoy the
country and being close to the earth. In boots and
tweeds, they revel in the open air and love to have
their dogs following at their heels. Richard Adams,
who created a new animal fiction genre with
Watership Down, set, of course, in the countryside, is
Taurus, and so is William Horwood, author of
Duncton Wood and other animal books. H. E. Bates,
who wrote about the countryside and its people, was
Taurean, and so is Phil Drabble, television's
countryman. Charlotte Brontë drew her inspirational
strength from the Yorkshire moors, to write a very
Taurean book where virtue and fidelity are rewarded
by true love and material security. Edward Jenner,

who developed the cowpox vaccine from cows (which later developed into the modern smallpox vaccine), was Taurean.

The Venusian Taureans are artistic and creative, cherishing beautiful things and designing and making them, too. Art, cinema, theatre, fashion shows, exhibitions, parties, they love creating them or attending them (Clive Barnes, drama critic of the New York *Post*, is Taurean) and being the most gifted hostesses and hosts is their metier. Whether Earthy or Venusian, they can apply their talents practically. They also like to plan ahead and prefer to know what is imminent. Surprises unsettle them.

There are of course, some Taurean failings: stubbornness, sticking in the same old rut rather than taking a chance, the rare but terrible temper when roused, acquisitiveness for the sake of it, obsession with money and possessions to the exclusion of people, dullness, never knowing when they are being boring, no sense of humour, self-obsession, a rigid perfectionism (common to all three Earth signs). Sometimes the latter bears wonderful fruit, as with Fred Astaire.

What you may take for Taurean obsession with money may be nothing more than their need for security, their need to know exactly where they stand in the world. Money in this case is their talisman, the Solomon's Circle that shields them from the worst of emotional adversity. Outsiders may think that the Taurean is stolid, phlegmatic, even unfeeling, but their passions run deep and they care with a fervour that puts the cooler signs to shame. Nothing is too much trouble for them, from the tiniest seedling to the largest tree; they will love and tend it all, and need the powerful vibrations of Earth beneath their feet. For this reason, they are not happy air travellers, and lifts, tall buildings and concrete pavements that shut out the Earth's magnetism fill them with unease and drain their vitality. Being practical, however, they will soldier on in such circumstances, but cannot wait to return to their own little plot, where the flowers bloom brighter, the leaves are greener and the air sweeter than anywhere else in the world. This is the green-fingered sign, but I would put it more strongly: Taureans have green hearts overflowing with richness and nourishment that animals, plants and people can soak up and be strengthened by. Whether male or female, they are the embodiment of Hathor herself.

They enjoy dancing – Fred Astaire and Margot Fonteyn are two fine examples. Hathor was goddess of dance, love and music, her attributes later being assimilated by Venus Aphrodite. Music can soothe the Taurean's savage breast but it must be romantic or classical: nothing avant garde or experimental. Home-loving to a fault, they can sometimes become literally housebound, immovable and unwilling to step beyond their front doors. (The sacred bulls were revered and worshipped, but they were prisoners nonetheless.) Finding plenty to do in their homes, Taureans will never be bored, and their houses will be a delight to visit, full of beautiful things, many of them hand-made, flowers and plants, embroidery, antiques, pictures, lace, collages, carved boxes and curios.

The danger is that Taureans can come to a halt when life is too comfortable and there are no more challenges. That old rut can look all too cosy and appealing. On occasion, rather than be disappointed or rejected, they may hide their ambitions and desires and outwardly appear flourishingly content, pressing their hurts and longings into the carved sycamore*

* The sycamore was sacred to Hathor.

box of their heart so that no one ever suspects what lies there. Needless to say, such repression is not good for their health and they must learn to let it all hang out now and again. Primal therapy is a little harsh for their tastes, yet something of that ilk is needed. Gentle hypnotherapy could be the answer, stripping off all those outer layers of pain and torment so that the emotions can unfold and blossom. Being a Taurean is very much about blossoming and bearing the fruit that all can enjoy.

The Taurus child

Taurean children are quieter than most and naturally well-behaved, but it may not seem so when they are determined to get their own way and refuse to change their minds. It is always better to defuse the situation rather than engage in head-on battle. They need a great deal of affection and will give plenty in return. They love reading and painting, and as they have an aptitude for their mother tongue they enjoy crosswords and quizzes. As they soon put on weight, their diet needs to be watched right from the start. White sugar in their feeds, or fruit juices or drinks sweetened with sugar, will upset their metabolism for good. Fruit, fresh and dried, nuts and crudités are the answer. These may have to be prepared artistically to make them attractive, but that is infinitely preferable to having an obese child who is the brunt of teasing at school and loathes PE. I know a Taurus child who used to go round draining people's teacups to get at the sugar dregs: believe me, this is the beginning of a steep and sticky slope with this food-loving, sweet-toothed sign. Like Librans, they need natural, high-fibre foods more than most. A word of warning about fruit juices: even the sugar-free ones are extremely concentrated in a way that Nature does not offer. Many oranges or apples go into one box of juice, far more than one could comfortably eat at one sitting. This is a strain on the pancreas in the same way as sugar, so the Taurean child's fruit juices should be diluted with mineral water, half and half. In infancy, dipping his or her dummy in honey would mean that minute pancreas struggling to cope with a concentration of sweetness. It can soon give way under the strain.

A Taurus child needs a much gentler pace of life than the Aries and Gemini child, who enjoy hurtling through time. Young Taureans need encouragement and the assurance that they are loved. They may lack confidence and be extremely shy, giving the impression that they are stupid, when this is far from the case. Artistic and practical, like Virgoans, their skills can be put to good use in the classroom, whether it is for decorating it or assembling and caring for the coin collection. Also like Virgoans, they can take longer than many children to come out of their shells, yet they often have an old head on young shoulders. Because of this, it is probable that they will be heaped with worries and responsibilities that they are truly too young to deal with. If they are taken too much into their parents' confidence, the burden will just add to their weight. They will rush to sweet foods to comfort themselves, while adopting a reassuring adult facade so that no one ever suspects the turbulence beneath.

As they are slow to change, it is better to raise them with as expansive a view as possible, encouraging them to take an interest in new ideas so that the familiar rut doesn't enclose them. Regular exercise of some kind is essential: so it is better if this becomes an early habit with them. They will enjoy artistic exercise such as ballet and *tai chi*, country dancing and gentle aerobics to music, cycling in the country-side, and gardening (although much of it doesn't use many calories, digging is an excellent exercise, as are building rockeries and fishponds and carrying potted plants and watering cans around.)

Health

The Taurean rulership of the throat and thyroid gland is the reason why Taureans so often have a weight problem. A bull gets very little exercise apart from its marital duties and the occasional charge across a field when angered. Similarly, Taureans find it very hard to work up enthusiasm for walking or playing squash or swimming. Cycling might well be the answer, because they can sit while they do it. The luxury of a jacuzzi, or an indulgent visit to a health farm would suit them, too, if they can afford it. If not, then it has to be the cycling, or dancing to their favourite music. Mother Nature's green bounty restores them and reminds them of their closeness to the Earth. If they are confined to the city for their work, then country trips are essential.

The weak spot the throat needs careful tending. Colds seem to settle there, and the pain of a septic throat is excruciating. Harsh antiseptic gargles should be avoided, and so should straining while singing. Smoking, of course, is foolhardy, and so is living or working in the company of smokers. Extra vitamin C is vital when mixing with others; at least 1g should be taken before all social occasions. Raw honey and lemon juice, gently heated (heat kills vitamin C) makes a soothing drink, and chewing honeycomb is also protective. Bees seal their combs with propolis, and this can now be bought as pastilles and lozenges. Cinnamon lozenges can help, too – and Olbas oil.

Raw dark brown sugar beaten with a little butter used to work wonders on my Taurean daughter's throaty cough when she was a child, but this is a remedy I wouldn't advise except in extreme need. When coughing, drinking plenty of water is one of the best lung restoratives. Children can be given blackcurrant tea, sweetened with raw honey. Use one teaspoonful of crushed currants to a cup of warm water. It is better for them to abstain from food if tonsillitis is threatening, and rest in a warm bed, drink natural cough mixtures, diluted fruit juices and herb teas.

If throat problems recur, it is time for Taureans to rethink their diet, eat more raw salads and fruits and raw or lightly cooked vegetables, increase their intake of vitamins A and C, get more exercise in the fresh air and, if necessary, see a herbalist, naturopath or Chinese-trained acupuncturist about making further improvements.

A raw-food diet with lots of fresh vegetables and fruit is probably the last thing Taureans hanker for. They like French delicacies, wine and butter and sugary puddings. Garlic is a good protector, a natural antiseptic and antibiotic, so if they do not like the taste, they should try to adapt to it gradually. Odourless garlic perles taken at night are the easiest way to absorb the benefits. Halibut or cod-liver oil capsules are the simplest way of taking extra vitamin A and D.

Leon Petulengro's grandmother, Anyeta, said, 'Stand on any hill and look for miles around at the view. There you will see God's bounty growing, just for the taking . . . plentiful. In everything that grows, we find the mystery of life a million times.' Taureans should think of these words next time they reach for a sugary, stodgy processed treat. There is no mystery of life in a boiled sweet or a bagel!

A silk or nylon scarf wound round the throat soothes soreness. The throat should always be covered out of doors if it is feeling raw or scratchy, and it is advisable not to change temperatures suddenly, but to stay in one room where possible and rest. Taureans will probably enjoy this more than any other sign! Red sage is an old and well-tried remedy for soreness, and gargling with sage extract in warm water a few times a day is recommended.

If the thyroid gland is underactive, then an anti-stress programme is essential for Taureans. First, a daily relaxation sequence. This might involve yoga breathing (quite simple to learn), autohypnosis, total relaxation to music, or walking in the fresh air. Each night, just before falling asleep, they should visualise themselves as lithe and slim, and repeat this visual-isation during the day, too. They should not say, 'I am going to be slim!' but, 'I *am* slim!' Cutting down on tea and coffee, and taking a B50 vitamin pill morning and evening, natural kelp in powder or tablet form for the iodine, zinc and a multi-vitamin is advisable so is 2–3 g of vitamin C, always with water or diluted fruit juice; it is destroyed by tea, coffee, alcohol and nicotine. Higher doses can be taken without harm. The sign of taking it in excess is diarrhoea, so if this happens, the dosage should be cut back. 1–2 tablespoons of fresh raw wheatgerm and 3 tablespoons of brewer's yeast daily. (If the powder is unpalatable, tablets are available.) Small, regular meals are better for the blood sugar than skipping meals and then gorging uncontrollably. Proteins, high-fibre foods, oats and oatmeal and complex carbohydrates maintain the level of blood sugar. If it is possible to get away from it all, then all the better. Soaking up sunlight and fresh air is greatly healing. Positive thinking, as with all ailments, is vital. If they feel that they will never get their energy back, and that they will never lose that excess weight, then they never will. When Taureans get down-hearted, they tend to expect the worst, but isn't that being illogical?

Illness can often be a time for taking stock, for looking at one's life in a clear light. If they have been burning the candle at both ends and gorging on high-calorie foods and chocolates to assuage their hunger, then it won't be surprising if they feel exhausted and their glands let them down. Would anyone put water in the car's petrol tank and expect it to start? Think of what sugar does to engines: it ruins them. The human body is a very sophisticated engine. It should not be abused with processed foods, sugar and salt-rich snacks.

Herbal teas for Taurus

Any flower teas, organically grown and naturally prepared, especially rose. Mint, peppermint or sage tea to combat the effects of overindulgence. Morning Starter by Jill Davies, to wake up. Apple tea for hoarseness of the throat due to infection. Sage tea for sore throats.

3

GEMINI

> To travel hopefully is a better thing than
> to arrive, and the true success is to
> labour.   *Robert Louis Stevenson*

> The zodiac is like a jigsaw: all the pieces
> have to be there for the right picture to
> emerge.   *Bernard Fitzwalter*

Gemini the Twins: c. 23 May–c. 21 June   Element:
Air. Planetary ruler: Mercury. Physical rulership:
lungs and arms, nervous system. By polarity with
Sagittarius: the hips and thighs.

Destiny of Gemini: to cheer those around them, and
to reduce the amount of inconsequential chatter.

Herbs for Gemini: valerian (a tonic of this is very
restorative for the nervous system), lavender, dill,
common parsley, mulberries, licorice, cow parsnip,
pomegranate, southernwood, mandrake, common
garlic, cress, caraway.

Vital vitamins and minerals for Gemini: B complex for
that taut nervous system (B12 helps to relax and
soothe the nerves and prevents pins and needles in
the arms; B6 feeds the nervous system). Folic acid
calms the mind. Vitamins C and A for healthy lungs
and to fight infection. Calcium and magnesium to
soothe and calm (always choose a chelated variety
for better absorption).

Gems for Gemini: amethyst, tortoise shell (the god
Mercury had a musical instrument made from this),

topaz. The ancients believed that the amethyst protected against drunkenness so they carved their drinking goblets from it. The amethyst was one of the gems in the breastplate of the Jewish high priest in ancient times. To Christians it symbolises humility and modesty and is a protector of chastity.

The myth behind the motivation

Romulus and Remus, famous for being suckled by a she-wolf, pursued an early career as cattle rustlers. When they were brought before the authorities, they pleaded their cause so cleverly and cogently that their true identity was revealed. Ever since, this sign has been associated with verbal skills. Born to a vestal virgin, Rhea Silvia, niece of the king, their father being the god Mars, the illicit twins had been left to die in the open, despite their royal connections. One can understand the great bond there must have been between the two abandoned and disowned boys. Geminians still have this deep emotional need for a soulmate. It may be their mother or sister or brother when they are young, and if they are fortunate, their marriage partner will later fit the bill. If they do not find that soulmate, then their life may be a rootless, promiscuous quest with little emotional satisfaction. There is still the connection between Mars and Gemini: many Ariens have Geminian or strongly Mercurial children. Rhea is one of the names for the Great Goddess, and Virgoans often have children born under this sign, too. The wolf was one of the Goddess's sacred animals: not hard to see here the true meaning behind the legend of the twins being suckled by a she-wolf.

Another pair of twins were Narcissus and his sister. Narcissus has had an extremely bad press because of his supposed vanity. In fact, he had an identical twin sister, whom he loved devotedly, and they would hunt together. When she died he was stricken, and haunted their old hunting grounds, gazing into pools and fountains to see her reflection in his own. This can explain much of the self-involvement of Gemini, who seems so egocentric at times and yet who craves that essential soulmate.

Castor and Pollux, the sky twins, were worshipped by the Spartans, their symbol being two vertical wooden bars crossed with two more. This is the origin of the astrological sign for Gemini. The sky twins were fathered by Zeus, the King of the Gods, and borne by Leda, another personification of the Great Goddess. One twin was immortal, one human. When Castor died in battle, the immortal Pollux was so grief-stricken that Zeus reunited them in the firmament, as the eternal twins.

As if still seeking those starry heavens, Geminians dislike being housebound. Mythologically, they were always thoroughly occupied in some way. All of them adore jaunts and journeys and outings. Anticipation is adrenaline to them. The average nine-to-five routine does not appeal and can be stifling. They may change jobs many times, happily keep two jobs going, or enjoy work-sharing because it breaks up monotony. Unable to display surges of emotion easily (which does not mean that they don't have them) Gemini often chooses an emotional mate: possibly one born under Cancer, who can exhibit for them all the highs and lows that they keep so well hidden themselves. Extravagant shows of feeling embarrass them; they cannot handle in-depth emotional discourses; nor do they practise great introspection. If it isn't there on the surface, then they don't want to dredge it up. Let sleeping emotions lie might well be their motto. This too might be a hangover from the day when grief so affected Pollux that his father placed him in the skies beside the brother he mourned so deeply. A lofty position, yes, but one that does rather immobilise! Being paralysed (as they see it) by a flood of emotion is not a happy thought for a Gemini. They would prefer to be very cool and nonchalant.

To the Greeks, Mercury was Hermes, messenger of the gods, with wings on his helmet and feet. He was also the protector of travellers, merchants and thieves. Getting there was his main aim, and he could communicate with all classes on all levels, from highest to lowest. Thoth, the ancient Egyptian counterpart of Hermes, taught the gods to write: he was a master of magic and medicine, with a mysterious depth to him that can only be guessed at by modern minds. Gemini can plumb this depth if they choose to do so – if they can pause and reflect and meditate. At worst, they can plunge into dishonesty and double dealing, applying their sharp minds to tricking, thieving and cheating – but this is the most negative aspect of the sign.

Eternal Peter Pans, bouncing with wit (Bob Hope, Bob Monkhouse and Gene Wilder are good examples), they flit their way through life, ad-libbing and joking, filling other people's existence with light and humour and a whacky outlook on life, but when dire problems come along, sometimes you may find that your charming elf has fled (if they are of the negative type). They do not settle easily to marriage unless fortunate enough to meet their soulmate early, and although brilliant communicators, their cool, suave facade can block deeper interchanges, causing those they meet to think that their wit, charm and loquaciousness is all there is to them – but they would be very wrong.

The Jungian shadow principle* can be seen in the famous split-personality that Gemini can display at its worst: the charmer on one side of the coin, the villain on the other. When this coin is tossed, it is Gemini's trusting friends and acquaintances who end up in a spin. My restless, energetic Birman cat is Geminian and she has two distinct sides: aloof and adventurous in the day, and dependent and affectionate in the evening. People who have seen her in daytime cannot believe the change that comes over her at night! The change with the human Gemini is not always so predictable. Some can be charming and fun for a day, or two or three days, and then suddenly along comes the alter ego, moody, difficult, discontented, unresponsive: the Mr Hyde of poisoned-potion fame. They can actively dread the appearance of their mythical twin, fearing that being possessed by them will be too distressing, too upsetting; but it is only the hidden, unacknowledged shadow that causes damage, and as the shadow twin is determined to appear, it is wiser to allow it the freedom to do so. Hide it, and Gemini is more likely to become Mr or Mrs Hyde. Face it, and they will become whole and better balanced. Meditation (which in their haste and impatience Geminians my find very difficult at first) will help this symbiosis. Reading about the Jungian shadow can be helpful, too.

The bird that is this sign's symbol can not only give its subjects superb voices but a brilliant gift for mimicry (Faith Brown, Mike Yarwood, Stanley

* The shadow, according to Carl Jung, is the unexpressed hidden side of the personality, those aspects that we cannot, or do not wish, to face. We are only whole when we have fully integrated our shadow, but this is not an easy task, hindered as it is by the projecting on to others of those aspects deep within ourselves that we do not acknowledge.

Baxter). Impersonating people is an art form with them; sometimes the less scrupulous ones impersonate others so that they can achieve their crooked aims. The witty one-liner, or the cheery comment, is also a pointer to recognising this sign; think of the way talking birds deliver their lines! Communicating is Gemini's major objective, and this could be through journalism, writing articles or books, radio, (many DJ's are born under this voluble sign), the press (at one time all the major editors in Fleet Street were Geminians) or international relations (Henry Kissinger and Terry Waite both display the Mercurial ability for relaying and receiving messages). Or they may perform on stage internationally, like Isadora Duncan and Josephine Baker. Geminian monarchs wish their country to expand and encourage foreign contacts, like Queen Victoria or Peter the Great (who had the Geminian height and dark good looks, as did Charles II, who was forced to travel extensively during Cromwell's reign). John F. Kennedy, too, was Gemini, with the winning smile, abundant energy, gift for oratory and foreign affairs associated with this sign; his charisma was due to his Libra ascendant. Singing like a bird, with the Gemini lungs, is another of their great gifts: Judy Garland, Jeanette MacDonald, Beverly Sills, Nancy Sinatra, Tom Jones, Cilla Black, Moira Anderson, Paul McCartney, Dean Martin, Barry Manilow and Alison Moyet are Geminians, as was Cole Porter, who wrote the songs.

Communications barons Lord Beaverbrook and Robert Maxwell were born under this sign, too. Investigative journalism involving travel suits them, for they can stay cool under fire, but if they do not acknowledge that their nerves can sometimes be shaken by such work, then they will suffer as a result. Conan Doyle, a Geminian, created Geminian

Sherlock Holmes, who uses his wits, reason and perception to solve crimes. Many of the actors who have played Holmes have also been Geminians, or Mercury ruled. Marion Zimmer Bradley, prolific fantasy, letter and short-story writer, is famous for her Darkover series, which is centred round the clash between two cultures, two viewpoints. Gemini authors are frequently prolific, as with Lena Kennedy and Catherine Cookson (born on the Gemini–Cancer cusp and writing about families). Or they may have two faces, as with Donald W. Campbell, who had a major role, in the formative years of science fiction, as editor and encourager of some of the future great writers of that genre, while also writing under his own name. He also wrote under the pen name Don A. Stuart, and he soon became, as Lester del Ray called it, 'the two most popular writers of science fiction.' This could only happen to a Gemini!

The tall, slender, talkative Geminian is likely to be a mine of information, never stuck for a word, lively, restless, curious, witty, sharp, knowledgeable and wonderful company. Needing little sleep but difficult to wake when they are resting, they effervesce through life, full of enthusiasms and action, their bright, bird-like eyes missing nothing. They are always young at heart and full of life. Joan Collins, a double Gemini, has removed the barriers of age for modern woman. Errol Flynn had all the Gemini charm and mental acuity, but he was an example of the negative aspect of the sign: restless, changeable, unreliable. Queen Victoria, ascendant, moon and sun in Gemini, wrote letters and diaries prodigiously and was an excellent example of the Gemini who is interested in everything and everyone, and dabbles in much. Logical and airy, they approach everything with a bright detachment, which can work well for everyday matters but not for love affairs. Geminians hate being ruffled, hate anyone to see the truth beneath their cool and competent exteriors, or suspect that they have emotions.

Blue-eyed, they have dark to black hair, pale Mercurial skins, long arms and legs, bright eyes, flashing grins and straight eyebrows. Sometimes, their noses may be hooked like a bird's beak, but there is also a beautiful baby-faced Geminian (Marilyn Monroe). Their fingers are long and straight and they move their arms and hands rapidly while talking. Josephine Baker had the typical Gemini build. Their voices are either very deep or high-pitched, and may sometimes be of varying, uneven timbre.

The Gemini child

A good education is more important to this child than to any other. They can be the most appealing companions, amiable and chatty, full of fun and never dejected. The love quizzes and crosswords and games; they love annotating things, making lists and notes. They were born for the age of the computer and universal communications. Parents may never see their Geminian child cry, but this does not mean that their feelings don't run deep. It is just that they are skilled at concealing them. That cool exterior may need a little working at while they are small, but by their teens they will have it perfected. It can be baffling to their loved ones. They can appear so passionless that parents may feel they have wasted a lifetime of love and devotion on a child who is incapable of loving them or responding. But this is misleading. They have their feelings; they are grateful; they do care. They will keep in touch when they leave home – perhaps more than many other signs.

Because they like to dabble in virtually everything, they need careful guidance as they grow, regular discipline, and encouragement to finish what they start. They will have 'crazes' which will last for a few weeks to six months, until a new craze takes its place. During these times they should be well supplied with information on their new interest so that they learn everything possible about it before the novelty wears off. It is worthwhile buying them books and pens and pencils, paper, magazines and paints, dictionaries and encyclopaedias. One day, they may write their own. (Example: Margaret Drabble.) Their endless questions may be exhausting at times, but they need to know. This is where all those books and magazines come in useful: and there are always exhibitions, museums and galleries to explore, and sporting events. The male Gemini is usually successful at sport. Tall and lithe, he can be a terrific advantage in the basketball team, or at heading the ball, and his long arms can be wonderful at saving goals and batting balls – as with Bjorn Borg, five times Wimbledon champion and as cool as they come.

They do overtire themselves and get irritable. If they suddenly go quiet, that is the sign they have overdone it. They may want to stay up late and may be capable of it, but parents must tell them how important sleep is for such a lively mind. All that growing is done at night, and Geminians grow tall, so they need their sleep. They should settle with a book at least once a day, for that is the most relaxed their mind will ever be during daylight. They can't sit still and do nothing. Music will soothe them too, and they may have a good, strong voice. In their teens they frequently get involved in pop groups. A cat or dog will help them to relax (stroking animals has been shown to lower blood pressure and relax the body considerably) and playing with a puppy or kitten is one of the Gemini child's delights.

Parents should not make fun of them or sneer at their interests. They are deeply sensitive, well-meaning individuals. They can also weigh people up in three seconds and be spot on.

Fast food was made for Geminians, and yet it is the last thing they should eat. Once in a while, maybe, but only if they are eating a nourishing diet normally. They need minerals more than most, plus vitamins and organic salts, and a raw-food diet is best for them. Unfortunately, many of them love meat, but this is a very limited choice. If they must eat it, it should be accompanied by a variety of greens and vegetables. Prone to allergies and sensitive reactions to additives and colourings, they can suffer asthma and chesty complaints. All highly coloured children's foods and sweets are to be avoided; those bright reds, browns and oranges are poison to Gemini. Spring water is the healthiest drink for them, and this infant needs to be breast-fed more than most. As their appetite can be small, it is vital that what they eat is not harmful or denatured, and they should not be allowed to fill up on empty calories. Coke and hot dogs are for treats only. The phosphorus in soft drinks weakens the bones and makes the nerves jittery; the hot dogs are full of colouring and chemicals; the white bread is filling without offering any health advantages. Geminians need wheatgerm and brewer's yeast, sesame and sunflower seeds, wholegrains, and lots of raw salads and vegetables.

The Geminian child must not be allowed to become a faddy eater. The bird is this sign's symbol, and Geminians can be the fussiest, choosiest eaters with

a worryingly small appetite. They can also go off
their food when worried or anxious. A daily multivitamin is essential. So is B complex. If they go off
their food after a bad bout of flu, three garlic perles
three times a day can bring back their appetite. If
they have lost weight, they also need bananas (full
of minerals), jacket potatoes, wholemeal cereals, milk
(goat's milk if they are allergic to cow's, which they
may well be), live yoghourt flavoured with fresh
fruit, and sugarless cakes made with dried fruit,
wholegrain flour and butter.

Health

Gemini rules the lungs, arms and nervous system.
Tension and overexertion can strain their delicate
nervous systems and they may take some time to
recover. They do not have the phlegmatic approach
of Taurus. (St Bernadette of Lourdes had Gemini
rising and was asthmatic: her poor origins and diet
would not have helped.) Regular rest, a little meditation or simple yoga breathing brings rich rewards.
B complex is the major vitamin for them as it protects
the nervous system. The advice given for the Gemini
child goes for the adult, too, and if they have had a
lifetime of eating the wrong foods, then I suggest a
one-day fast on spring water and fruit. On this day,
they can eat as much fruit as they wish, keeping to
one variety for each meal, and between meals, drink
as much water as is comfortable. A practitioner
should be consulted before fasting in case there is
any condition that it would act against. If they are
taking any medicines, they should see a nutritionally
trained naturopath before water-only fasts. Headaches, nausea and a feeling of illness may hit during
the fast day, but this is the poisons coming out and is

beneficial. If they stick it out, the result is a wonderful feeling next day, of being light and fresh and clean. Then it's time to start the new dietary regime, and vow never to gorge on junk foods again, or fill the freezer with ice cream (eating ice cream, especially at night, is bad for all signs) and other junk foods. Geminians should not buy Coke, but blend their own fresh fruit and vegetable juices and make their own sugar-free snack bars. Bananas are one of the healthiest fast foods if they are not overweight. They can add a little extra greenery to every meal, to sandwiches, to meat dishes, making sure it is fresh greenery. It should not be cut with a knife as this releases the enzymes that destroy its vitamin C. There are excellent homeopathic remedies for strained nerves and overactive minds and insomnia. Local health food shops should stock them; or a homeopathic practitioner can be consulted.

Eating wisely and taking a herbal tranquilliser when under extra stress should be part of the regular Geminian routine. B complex pills daily are obligatory for this highly strung sign.

Fish is an ideal food for that busy brain, and sesame seeds are full of soothing calcium. So are milk, cheeses, yoghourt, nuts, tinned fish and alfalfa. If insomnia is a problem, Geminians should ask these questions: do they drink tea or coffee in the evenings? This can overstimulate the mind. So too can cocoa and drinking chocolate, and heavy smoking is one of the major causes of insomnia. Smokers are living on adrenaline and simply cannot switch it off. Chamomile tea is a soothing nightcap, and a herbal pillow of hops is easily employed. That old-fashioned remedy, warm milk with a little raw honey and a few raisins to eat, should make them sleep better. If they don't have a weight problem, a light, nourishing snack in the evening will ensure that the blood sugar doesn't drop too low and make for restlessness. There are many excellent herbal sleeping pills and relaxants at local health shops, too. Drugs should be avoided, as they cause more problems than they cure. The fear of missing out on something is often behind the Gemini disinclination to relax or retire at a suitable time. They hate being out of touch or not hearing the latest news. Yet rest ensures that they will enjoy another bright and fruitful busy day. A bad night means that they will be bleary and irritable and unable to relish communications. They should be gently reminded of this by their loved ones. Do not indulge them if they have been burning the candle at both ends yet again. It is not something to be proud of and they should learn not to do it. After all, it is their nearest and dearest who are left to pick up the pieces, and a jigsaw Gemini is not a pretty sight! That vital missing piece is all too often a healthy nervous system.

Getting into the Land of Nod across the enormous chasm caused by the possession of such an alert and overactive mind is part of the problem for Gemini. Simple deep breathing, autohypnosis, counting sheep (this has a hypnotic effect) all help to bridge this chasm. If these fail, they can start over again; or try counting the sheep backwards; holding a deep breath for a count of five, then breathing out to a count of five. They should not read overexciting books last thing at night, and the same goes for watching horror films on television.

Herbal teas for Gemini

Any relaxing and soothing teas such as chamomile, valerian, balm. For intermittent coughs: thyme. Stubborn cough or asthma: carrot tea. For breathlessness:

valerian. For bronchial problems or mental strain: apple. Make sure that flowers, fruits and vegetables are organically grown and naturally prepared, as Geminian lungs and nervous systems are susceptible to artificial additives.

4

CANCER

The female is symbolised in astrology
by the moon . . . there is a very close
archetypal link between the orbit of this
planet and the feminine polarity of our
personality, regardless of the nature of
our sex.   *Robin MacNaughton*

Archaic Man saw an earthly counterpart
for everything that happened in the
heavens, with Man himself as the centre
of the universe. With the first breath
of infancy he internalised these cycles
. . . until death, he and the universe
were one. And what happened in the
heavens was first marked by the cycles
of the eternal Moon.
Jerry J. Williams, American astrologer
and attorney

Moonchild (Cancer the Crab): c. 22 June–c. 22 July
Element: Water. Planetary ruler: the Moon. Physical
rulership: the breasts, stomach and alimentary canal.
By polarity with Capricorn: sluggish circulation.

Destiny of Cancer: to spread romance and fantasy. To
house the homeless. To turn sadness into beautiful
creativity.

Herbs for Cancer: daisy, agrimony, balm, common
garden lettuce, cucumber, moonwort, mouse-ear,
white poppy, wild poppy, privet and purslane.

Vital vitamins and minerals for Cancer: B complex to
keep the blood-sugar level and for a healthy diges-

tion; vitamin E and oil of evening primrose to protect the breasts. Vitamin A for gastric ulcers.

Gems for Cancer: pearl, moonstone, white opal, silver, chalcedony. In China, the pearl is considered the symbol of talent, and porcelainware is decorated with pearls to be given to great poets and writers. It is a beautiful, gleaming jewel that requires tender care and should be worn next to the skin to maintain its sheen. In the New Testament, the pearl represents the Gospel. The Angel Gabriel was instructed to give his protection to those who carried the pearl, which was considered to be the major gem of the Christian religion (Pearls of Wisdom). Mother-of-pearl is the Madonna herself. *Margarita*, Latin for pearl, has come down to us as margarine, because the early form of substitute butter was pearl-coloured.

The myth behind the motivation

Moonchildren are not like others. Deeper and more emotional, they are vessels for all the dreams and yearnings, myths and memories of our past. Here we see the Great Mother as Moon Goddess and creator, for the Moon that rules birth and the ebb and flow of life was her major symbol. Cows and bulls were worshipped not only for their earthy fertility but because their horns are like the crescent Moon. Horseshoes are considered lucky even today because of the ancient belief that their prongs resemble the new Moon, bringer of good fortune from the benevolent Mother of All. Crabs have crescent-shaped pincers; as the tides wash in and out, controlled by the Moon's magnetism, the crabs are revealed, scuttling about in sandy pools. They too appear to be Moon-ruled, which is one of the reasons why they were adopted for this sign.

The bountiful Great Mother was worshipped worldwide in many forms. As Freya, she was the Scandinavian Mother Earth, from whose name came the title Frau. Freya's carriage was drawn by cats, and the Greek Cybele's chariot was drawn by lions. In ancient Crete, the Earth Goddess was Goddess of Animals as well as protectress and nourisher of human beings. The boar mask worn by Freya's Baltic followers protected them against all harm, and the boar or sow was closely connected with her; in Egypt, pigs were sacred to Isis. Freya rode on Hildeswin, the boar with golden bristles. Think of the boar bristling with anger; how dangerous it looks, how hard. Cancerians can assume a tough exterior to hide their deep sensitivity. It isn't easy being a psychic sponge. Indeed, it can be very painful at times. Who can blame them for erecting that hard shell?

Pigs are just one of the many animals now treated with contempt but which were once sacred to the Goddess: the crow (shot as vermin), the wolf (feared, and their name given to sex-hungry men), the lion (hunted and endangered), the snake (made into boots and shoes to be trodden on) – there is still the powerful race memory of its Goddess symbolism that makes some people cower from it. Forget the Freudian connection; it was the most sacred symbol of the Goddess, and those ancient associations are embedded deeply in our subconscious – the pig (factory-farmed and raised in pens like slices of toast as if devoid of feeling), the cow (raised to be killed and its young torn from it so that humans can have her milk), the horse (slaughtered by the hundreds at the battlefront and now hard ridden over racetrack hedges, or beast of burden), the butterfly (driven to extinction by pesticides), the frog (hacked up for food and left for dead).

Many of the Goddess's animals are difficult if not

impossible to approach, or to treat as pets. They have tusks, sharp fangs, they bite, they sting, they're slimy or they wriggle, they eat carrion. There is always this distance, this element of caution and wariness involved. Isis is veiled for the very same reason: to keep that healthy distance between her and her worshippers. In Cancerians, and in Virgoans, who are also ruled by the Queen Goddess of the Harvest, this distance can be felt and is frequently misinterpreted as coldness, sometimes even as mercilessness. The truth is that beneath that shell, behind that bite, Cancerians are soft and romantic and tender. Try to keep that in mind when you get their famous cold-shoulder treatment, that tough-guy response. Barbara Stanwyck has spent her life playing tough, feisty heroines, yet she has a heart of gold. Sylvester Stallone has made a fortune playing 'rocky' parts, as did James Cagney and Harrison Ford, who is so home-loving a Cancerian that he has even built his own home. 'Mad Max' Mel Gibson has Cancer rising, but who would believe there was such sensitivity behind that steely expression?

Behind that mask or shell may be found some of the biggest hearts; people like Princess Diana, Dr Barnardo and Catherine Bramwell; people who care deeply for children, the homeless and the unfortunate. At their best they are caring mothers, fathers, husbands and wives, but at their worst, they cling and suffocate, harp on the past and bemoan their imagined ill treatment. There is something of the Sumerian Mother Goddess Inanna in the negative Cancerian. Inanna was the source of fertility, mate and mother to men, sometimes bringing them all that they most desired but at other times destroying them with her demands. Innana was all that was good and all that was bad, and even today mothers must take the brunt of this ambivalent male feeling towards

them, although its sacred origins are long forgotten.
The Christian Church adapted the passionate, pagan
Queen Goddess for its own usage, turning her into
the sanitised, saintly, immaculate Madonna (who is
now thankfully becoming recognised in a more
realistic way). The pagan Great Goddess was also a
virgin – this duality is far older than the Christian
Church – but she was a tripartite Goddess, and all
her aspects were acknowledged and revered.

The Christian age has been very idealistic, a time
of unreal demands and expectations, and no one has
suffered more from these than women, who have
been urged to deny their true natures and adopt
the virginal, one-dimensional cloak of Mary. In pre-
Christian times, the Mother was paramount, her son
and lover minor characters in the religious hierarchy.
With the arrival of Christianity, it was the first time
that the Son was superior to the Mother; it is an
unnatural placement, causing an imbalance, but it
was the Church's way of stripping the Goddess of
her power, magic and mystery – which they greatly
feared, and still do: witness the furore over women
priests.

In Milton's *Paradise Lost*, Astarte-Inanna was
portrayed as one of the fallen angels: '*Astoreth, whom
the Phoenicians called Astarte, Queen of Heaven, with
crescent horns; To whose bright image nightly by the moon,
Sidonian virgins paid their vows and songs.*' Usually
sculpted naked by her followers, she was portrayed
standing on a lion, a lotus bloom in her right hand
to symbolise eternal life, two serpents in her left
hand, for their skin-sloughing technique represented
the emergence of new life from old. In the Book of
Revelation, murder and lust are represented by the
great whore sitting on her scarlet beast and holding
in her hand a cup full of foulness and impurities.
Lilith was a she-demon personifying the lust and

carnality of woman, while Eve brought about man's downfall by tempting Adam. Hollywood has been greatly responsible for strengthening this view of woman as wicked, scheming and immoral, and the glut of films portraying prostitutes as victims of murderers is one way of publicising that men secretly feel woman should still be punished for her 'sinful' ways.

Add to this Christian distrust and antipathy the cyclical moods of the Cancerian's Moon and Water rulerships and you find a sign that is barely understood. Cancerians cannot help but display their varying moods, the good and the bad, but in doing so are a mirror of all that the Christian era has struggled to repress for two thousand years. Women do have moods! Women are emotional! And nowhere are they more moody and emotional than in the sign of Cancer. This is reality, however, not falsehood, and it is the problem of others to accept the true face of the true woman rather than deny and scorn it.

Cancerian men have found their emotional qualities an advantage, for although they excel at putting on the stiff upper lip, they have a skilled intuition and an emotional gut reaction that can be invaluable in business or wherever shrewd judgment is needed. Richard Branson is a prime example of this.

Cancerians have large, rounded, rich blue eyes and fair or blonde hair. Princess Diana is the perfect example of the beauty of this sign at its zenith, with her enormous rich blue eyes and fair colouring, sensitivity, compassion and deep interest in children. America's sun sign is Cancer and its ideal of beauty is blonde, blue-eyed and large bosomed. Holland, also blonde and blue-eyed, is Cancer ruled. The build is medium-boned, small to medium height, with round faces or square jaws. Kurt Russell, Adam Faith, Lena Horne, Diana Rigg, Shirley Cheriton,

David Hockney, Colin Wilson and Virginia Wade have the square jaw. Those who take after the new Moon are slender as reeds (Farrah Fawcett, America's ideal beauty for twenty years now, has Cancer rising), and Nancy Reagan and Meryl Streep both have this sun sign. Glenda Jackson is Cancer rising. Those who take after the full Moon tend to put on weight easily and can become quite rotund. Even when slender, this sign does not have a pronounced waistline (Jerry Hall and Debbie Harry). Cher, another of America's favourites, is Cancer rising, too, but she owes her exotic dark colouring to her Taurean sun sign. Having the moon near one's ascendant can sometimes cause a rotund shape, as with Queen Victoria in later years.

Cancerian science fiction author John Wyndham wrote of Cancerian extremes: the world being flooded, in *The Kraken Wakes*; blonde children with dangerous ESP in *The Midwich Cuckoos* (filmed as *Village of the Damned*).

The Cancer child

The Cancerian child, or those with the Moon prominently in their birthcharts, are dreamy, clinging, shy and fey, but behind that emotional facade is a sharp mind ably supported by strong intuition and possibly even stronger psychic powers. The Cancerian or Moon-ruled child will know intuitively when something is not right. They will sense when adults are not what they appear, but to puzzled parents this may seem like emotional nonsense. They can see right through people, feel the ulterior motives behind a false smile, and withdraw. When small they may not be able to bluff their way through such unnerving encounters and the result may be hurt feelings on both sides. As they develop their protective shell they will be able to handle that extremely difficult moment when they perceive the unpleasant truth about someone – maybe someone who has been brought into their life to play an important role. It is no fun being psychic when adults are telling you to befriend someone who makes your skin crawl! What if it is a new head teacher? Parents should listen to Cancerian children when they produce what seem to be amazing judgments out of thin air.

All this emotion, imagination and intuition needs careful handling by an adult let alone a child. Tears and storms can be the result of mishandling these sensitive, tender-hearted children. It is tragic if they have been so clumsily treated that they grow up encased in a rigid, immovable shell, for they will repel many with that hardness that appears to be cold-cut cynicism. They should have a cuddly pet to love and tend; they will be deeply attached to their mothers. Mothering, to them and from them plays a large part in their lives and always will. They need someone to wrap their arms around and love; someone who will love them in return. There will be many sobbing tears should anything happen to a pet they adore, and these must not be repressed. Mourning ceremonies should be encouraged and carried out with solemn ritual. Stifled grief can unsettle a Cancerian, child or adult.

The sooner the Cancerian child becomes involved in helping others the better. It may be animals or disabled children, or families in the Third World; it does not matter, as long as their emotions are invested in a valuable cause.

They may be particularly entranced by the Moon, lying in bed with their eyes fixed upon it. They need to be told that it is their ruling planet and that when it is full, they will be bursting with energy and maybe they will feel overemotional and irritable. When it is new, they should embark on new ventures and ideas, take up a new friendship or start their new school project or course. During the dark phase, in the few days before the new Moon, they should rest and reflect, and recharge their energies. They may feel tired or a little out of sorts then, or just lacking in enthusiasm, but their usual energies will return in a few days. It is wiser not to let Cancerian children attempt anything even slightly dangerous around a full Moon, for they will be vulnerable. They should never be operated on surgically during this time, or have any serious medical treatment except in an emergency. They are also more likely to fall or have minor accidents at full Moon, for their judgment can be affected and they can make silly mistakes. There is no need to worry them; parents should just make them gently aware, and impress upon them that they will be working with Mother Nature instead of against her if they heed this advice.

Learning to balance this turmoil of emotions is not always easy. Seeing things that others cannot see is also stressful; sensing the hidden truth about people is difficult to handle. Rather than become involved in the unpleasantness of public exposure, Cancerians hide behind their shells in a strategic retreat, rather like Librans who have Cancer at the top of their birthchart. When they feel that the water is right, they will cautiously put out a toe (or pincer) and emerge. Building up their protective auric shield is one of the first things that little Cancerians should be taught. It will help to put a barrier between them and all the pains and torments of the world around them.

Here is a simple aura-strengthening exercise: sit in a quiet room with the hands on the knees and feet together on the ground. Breathing deeply, relax the body, part by part, and imagine that you are surrounded by a bubble of colour. It can be white or blue, whichever you prefer. Imagine it encircling you, a beautiful protective sphere of light, completely airtight. Imagine the knot that fastens it and through which nothing can touch you. When this is firmly fixed in your mind, take time to enjoy the peace and calm you are feeling, before completing the exercise and becoming aware once again of the Earth beneath your feet. This can be practised once or twice a day until you can create this protective bubble instantly when the need arises, so that it becomes a habit. It is also far better protection than a pretend shell.

Health

Full Moons may well affect Cancerians deeply. It is better for them not to plan anything vital or unusual at these times, and better to be at home rather than travelling, especially if sea or air is involved. It is wiser to work with the cyclic energies of the Moon rather than to struggle against them, wiser to start new ventures at the new Moon, rest during the few days of the dark phase and complete projects at a full Moon. This is good advice for everyone but particularly for Cancerians. They may well find that the stresses ease, that they gain a flowing rhythmic sensation that is very comforting and reassuring. Why fight Nature?

Cancer rules the breasts and stomach, the nourishing part of womanhood. She feeds the young and sets them on their feet. They come to her for love and care and wisdom. Cancerians make sheltering, indulgent parents but they often neglect themselves. What use is it being wonderful parents if they fall ill? Remember those pagan worshippers: with their ancient rites and rituals they ensured that their Great Goddess stayed strong and undamaged. If the roots of the tree are weak, then the branches cannot flourish.

It is not healthy for Cancerians to try to cling to what is past, nor for them to be obsessed with memories; yet this is a tendency of the sign, which can be eased by Bach flower remedies if it becomes overpowering. If Cancerians are always looking back then they cannot take that vital step into the future.

A high-fat diet in injurious and, along with caffeine, is implicated in cystic disease of the breasts. High-fibre diets protect them. Cancerians enjoy good plain cooking, but too much cooked food is dead food, its protective enzymes destroyed. Fresh, raw food is best, and they should stay as near to Nature as they can with their diet. Chips and crisps, and pies made with white flour and hormone-packed meat, are as far from Nature as anyone can get. (See list of Foods from the Dead Zone in the appendix.) Oats and porridge, vegetables and wholegrains keep the blood sugar steady so that Cancerians can avoid the ups and downs of hypoglycaemia on top of the ups and downs of their Moon and Water rulership.

It would be incorrect to say that the Moon is inconstant. She may vanish, but she always returns, bright and new. Cancerians have extensive powers of recuperation, but this can only be effected with a good diet and relaxation. High stress, or the wrong adaptation to stress, also plays its part in breast troubles – as it does in cancer (the disease). Alcohol and tobacco steal vital nutrients and make every day a battle for the poor besieged body. Add to this internal stress the problems of coping with life today – traffic jams, pollution, constant bad news in the press and on television, the feeling that the world is becoming more dangerous, employment worries, loved ones falling ill – and you have a prime breeding ground for disease.

Vitamin E is the major breast protector, and vitamin A, or its precursor beta-carotene (found in red, yellow and orange vegetables), protects against cancer and infection. Vitamin E is found in wheat-germ (one of Nature's wonder foods), the oils of wholegrains, seeds and nuts, wholegrain rice, peanuts, oats, cabbage, spinach and broccoli. It is easily destroyed by refining, processing, heating, freezing, time, and exposure to air. Oils should be cold-pressed to ensure that they maintain their vitamin E content. Most supermarket oils are devoid of vitamin E, and many supposedly unsaturated 'health' margarines contain hydrogenated fat which destroys vitamin E. Avoid this type of fat. Thousands of women are dying of breast cancer every year.

Rushed meals and drinking while eating can upset the delicate Cancerian stomach. It is wisest not to drink for half an hour before a meal and at least half an hour after a meal as this dilutes the digestive acids. Stomach bloating may be a problem and this can be helped by eating slowly, never eating when rushed, chewing well and sticking to natural foods. Cancerians can put on weight easily and retain fluids. They can be slender like the new Moon or round like the full Moon; the latter soon lose their waist line and resemble a barrel if they overindulge (e.g. Henry VIII, Cyril Smith and Charles Laughton).

Herbal teas for Cancer

Mint and peppermint for digestive troubles and for the effects of overindulgence. Dandelion for sluggish digestion. Marjoram for excessive stomach acidity. Basil for stomach upsets. Evening Peace by Jill Davies for soothing sleep. Norfolk Punch at night when over-stressed. Chamomile by the London Herb and Spice Company.

5
LEO

Astrology is a game of mirrors: you look
at a mystery, it reflects another. Its
status is unique in the scale of scientific
values. A large part of its planetary
symbolism has been demonstrated to be
incontrovertibly, statistically true.
Michel Gauquelin, French scientist and
astrology researcher

The significance of astrology is that it
can transform the profane into the
sacred, the facts of astronomy into the
revelation of a cosmic order manifest
in the cell and the human person as well
as in the solar system and the galaxy.
Dane Rudhyar

Leo the Lion: c. 23 July–c. 22 August   Element:
Fire. Planetary ruler: the Sun. Physical rulership:
heart, gall bladder, spine. By polarity with Aquarius:
the circulatory system.

Destiny of Leo: to captivate and entertain. To take a
back seat now and again (however difficult!).

Herbs for Leo: saffron, chamomile, borage, bay leaves,
rue, eyebright, burnet, tormentil, walnuts,
dandelion.

Vital vitamins and minerals for Leo: B complex and
vitamin E protect the heart and circulation. Vitamins
C and B6 work together to keep the heart healthy,
as does vitamin F (polyunsaturated fatty acids) along

with fish oils. Fish should be eaten at least twice a week, preferably four times, to maintain a vigorous heart. A cocktail of all the minerals is essential for fully active heart health. Excess activity (for example, long-distance jogging) can drain the heart of minerals and cause collapse unless diet and supplementation is adequate.

Gems for Leo: topaz, jasper, yellow diamond, yellow amber. Jasper signifies faith to the Christian. In Christian art, yellow or gold represent the Sun, God's bounty, fruitfulness and fidelity.

The myth behind the motivation

The Sun is the fount of all life, the centre of our universe. If the weather is cloudy or grey, it affects our mood. When the Sun shines we all feel better. The Sun is not something that we can forget or ignore. We need it to live. Mother Earth would be barren without it (which is why the Sun God and Moon Goddess were so frequently lovers and worshipped together); crops would not grow, we would die of starvation. Those born under Leo are born with an innate sense of their own self-importance, pride and self-value. Like the planet that rules them, they want to be the centre of the universe; they like to be on stage all the time, the cynosure of all eyes, the recipient of flattery and praise, attention and appreciation. Without this, they wilt and can actually become depressed or ill. Approaching all things with a cheery heartiness, they can eventually exhaust themselves, but find it impossible to admit that they might be feeling depleted or below par. Their pride will not allow them to admit weariness or loss of vitality. They fear such a state as we fear the absence of sunlight and warmth. They can be very sorry sights when ill.

Apollo was enormously popular with the ancients. He had more than three hundred titles, including, 'god of radiance', 'slayer of wolves,' 'lizard slayer' and 'god of oracles'. He it was who overthrew the Earth Goddess, Gaia, slaughtering Python, Gaia's protector, and instilling himself and his omnipotent hero cult in her place at Delphi. Out went the Earth Goddess worship and in came the masculine-centred religion and male domination of the Sun God.

Ancient Persians made their vows by their king and the Sun God Mithras, who was identified with their monarch. Bull sacrifice was closely connected with the Mithraic cult and, from Mithras's unwilling sacrifice of a white bull, sprang the heavens, the zodiac and the fixed stars, while the white bull itself became the crescent Moon. From the bull's blood came trees and plants, vines, grain and the elements; from his semen, humankind and the animal kingdom. (Whatever the religion, the bull is always associated with fertility and strength.)

Is it any wonder that Leo sees himself as vitally important on the worldly stage, the centre and the source, the creator? Treat him as such and he will be benevolent, a glowing Sun. Neglect him, and it will be as if your own Sun has gone out. Apollo was the god of music, prophecy, archery and heroism, and his handmaidens, the Muses, had everything else safely tied up: Urania was Muse of astrology and astronomy; Clio, of history; Thalia, of comedy; Calliope, of epic poetry; Melpomene, of tragedy; Terpsichore, of choral dancing; Erato, of love poetry; Euterpe, of flute playing; Polyhymnia of mimic art. The Nine, as they were known, made life a brighter existence, filling it with light and joy and literacy. They refreshed and heartened, on Apollo's behalf.

However, originally they were worshipped as a Triple Goddess in their own right.

Despite his beauty, undoubted gifts and virtues, Apollo had a poor record with the opposite sex. His first love, Daphne, was happier to be turned into a laurel tree rather than submit to his lovemaking. The virgin Bolina threw herself into the sea rather than accept his advances. When Coronis was carrying his child, she betrayed him with another lover. Apollo killed her, but their child was saved by Mercury and became Aesculapius, the god of healing whose symbol was the caduceus, the serpent-entwined staff that is the emblem of the Medical Corps. Apollo gave Mercury the caduceus as a present. He gave Cassandra the gift of prophecy in exchange for her love, but she did not keep her part of the bargain. In revenge, he left her with the gift but ordained that no one would believe what she said. Sybil asked for eternal life if the Sun God became her lover; she got it, then spurned him. She kept her gift, but as she had not asked for eternal youth, she paid a terrible penalty. There is a moral in this for Leos. They should not fling themselves at people, positive that they are irresistible in all their arrogance and glory. A more subtle approach is needed for courtship.

Apollo also symbolised the abandonment of the feminine and the adoption of masculinity, reason and logic. Lacking female sensitivity and intuition, he blundered when it came to the arts of love. Since his reign began we have seen the unwelcome results of such behaviour, with men assuming the leading role and treading on female toes at every turn.

It is interesting that our two greatest female impersonators, Danny La Rue and Barry Humphries (Dame Edna Everage) are Leo and Leo rising. Of course, the love of plumage and bright colours comes into it, but it is almost as if they wish to recapture that lost femininity, besieged so long ago by Apollo when he dethroned Gaia.

Leo can also be blindly unseeing, despite all that light and brilliance – or maybe because of it. At his best he is the devoted family man and a generous, magnanimous husband, but he must have his dues. He must be adored, appreciated and revered; he must be the centre of the home. He likes his family around him, like the Muses in ancient times, beholden and grateful. He laps up flattery. George Bernard Shaw, a Leo, said, 'My speciality is being right when other people are wrong,' and, 'I often quote myself; it adds spice to my conversation.'

When kept in the dark or deliberately ignored or betrayed, the Lion can show his destructive temper and wreak havoc on those who have scorned him, his gifts turning to ashes in their hands, like the gifts he gave Cassandra and Sybil. The Sun that brings life and vitality can also scorch to a wasteland.

In more ancient times, the Lion was revered as the Great Goddess's beast. In this form, she could be gentle, as when associated with Bastet (from whose kittens we get the word bastard), or ferocious, as when associated with the lion-headed goddesses Sekhmet and Tefnut. When Bastet lost her temper, however, she could become savage. The Goddess had her chariot drawn by cats or lions, and it was the lion's ruff-like golden mane that inspired its link with the Sun. Sovereigns once sat on lion-faced thrones to signify their kingship and we can still see the remnants of this practice in the clawed legs found on thrones and antique chairs.

It is not surprising that Leo cannot take criticism, that he puffs up and blusters when fault is found with him. Once a king always a king. Once a queen always a queen. Do not expect a monarch to change his spots!

In Christian belief, the lion is associated with the hermit, possibly because it takes lion-hearted courage and dignity to live the hermit's life – especially if one is a Leo. (More suited now to Virgo, the lion has become the beautiful, serene domesticated cat, the companion of so many Virgoan writers.) The lion is a good parent, and so is Leo, protective, genial, putting aside his regality when romping with his little ones – and how he can roar if they are endangered.

This sign features prominently amongst male ballet dancers, giving them strength, dignity and regal bearing. Rudolf Nureyev is Leo rising, and his magnificent stage presence, his composure and pride are all Leo. Christopher Dean, partner of Jayne Torvill, is Leo, and so is Robin Cousins, and again the tall, majestic, stately demeanour is evident. The men can be very glamorous, too (George Hamilton, Robert Redford). The Leonine hair colouring can be any shade of the sun – yellow, golden, russet, tawny, pale gold – the texture usually being thick, and some-times quite coarse. The Leo hair is often very notice-able, either for being thick and abundant, brightly coloured, or even wild and untamed (Sally Beauman, Michael Foot, Lucille Ball, Andy Warhol, the Princess Royal, Mae West – who was famed for her pompa-dour hairstyle – and Barbara Windsor. Davy Crock-ett's hat took the place of his hair, but was just as famous; Napoleon Bonaparte also had a distinctive and unique hairstyle.) It often frames the face like a halo. Their eyes are a strong blue, and they have rounded, rather flattish features (like the lioness) with full mouths (P. D. James and Whitney Houston). Their dignity is much in evidence at all times, and they are generally well-built and tall – especially when Leo is on the ascendant. Leos have a habit of throwing out their chests proudly, more often seen in actors and actresses of the sign, such

as Madonna, Robert Mitchum and Mick Jagger. They
are frequently empire builders; Alfred Hitchcock,
Henry Ford, Cecil B. De Mille, Fidel Castro, Napo-
leon, Mussolini, the Prince Regent – a very Leonine
Leo – and Georgette Heyer, who recreated the
Regency era in fiction, were all Leos.

The Leo child

Leo children will be exuberant, hearty, enthusiastic,
noisy, energetic, bossy and self-centred. Their lordly
whims should not be indulged. It is up to parents to
teach them that natural lordliness means caring for
all creatures great and small, and to teach them to
share and to protect those who are weaker than
themselves. They will love acting and dressing up
and are naturals at being on stage. They will enjoy
asking friends round for tea when they can be
bountiful hosts or hostesses and officiate at the event.
But when the limelight deserts them, as it must at
times, they can descend into helpless depression –
or a temperamental sulk. They must learn that this
is immature and silly, and that everyone has to take it
in turns to have what they want. They are essentially
good-hearted and fair-minded, and can sometimes
even be taken advantage of.

Dancing, acting or taking the stage at any event
will please them enormously. Rarely do they suffer
stage nerves or fear the limelight. Parents have to
watch that they don't exhaust themselves and
become irritable, for they do not recoup their energies
quickly and can feel very sorry for themselves at such
a time. They need brightly coloured books, dressing-
up clothes and jewellery, paints and coloured pencils
and lots of paper to express themselves freely, and

a pet to lavish their warm hearts upon. They love flamboyant colours and ostentatious dressing.

Obesity can be a problem, and lounging about eating sweets and cakes won't help. Indulging them with fatty and sugary home cooking is doing them no favour. As a treat, yes, but daily, no. That could be laying down a lifetime of ill health for Leo children by getting them accustomed to high calorie, low-nourishment foods, for they are stubborn and strong willed and won't take to anyone suggesting dietary changes when they are adults. They get very set in their ways as time goes on, like Taureans, and nothing will make them see healthy sense. They could dig their graves with their mouths, so parents must see that they do not start them on that unhappy course.

Health

All that gusto and heartiness takes its toll. Being unable to admit that they might be wrong, or might not be as infallible as they think, can be a great strain. Leos love the good things of life – rich food and the best wines, sweet puddings, chocolates, liqueurs – but they pay the price for this. Overweight is the first symptom, and this causes strain on the spine (a Leo weak spot) and they get stiff backs, lumbago and inflammation. As they are a Fire sign, they can suffer fevers and feverish conditions. They usually crave the Sun, and feel out of sorts in winter.

Organising people and telling them what to do can be draining – especially as they don't always agree with Leonine commands! Bravado is essential when things aren't going too well, and again that takes a lot of psychic energy which could be employed in better ways. Sometimes allowing others to see the truth beneath all that bluff can only make Leos appear more human and likeable people.

Backs stay healthier if they are kept warm, so sunbathing shouldn't be done in a deckchair, which roasts the front while freezing the back. Tucking a small pillow between the thighs in bed at night can take the strain off the lower back. Lying flat on the back in bed is a strain on the spine. If he must, for this position is the one often assumed by Leo, who is lord of all he surveys, then he should keep a pillow beneath the knees. A hot bottle on an aching back can work wonders, carrying away toxins that irritate. Soft, unsupported seats should be avoided, and a firm cushion tucked in the small of the back to keep it upright. Deskbound Leos should never hunch, but sit upright, tuck in the small cushion and support the feet so that the thighs are a little higher than the hips, making sure that the desk height suits leg and hand height. Walking tones up the whole body, keeps muscles supple and carries away toxins. Aromatherapy can also help, and many back problems can be quickly cured by a registered osteopath or chiropractor. Acupuncture, too, has its part to play. Languishing on soft velvet cushions looks very becoming but it offends the spine and the heart muscles. Lumbago has responded to high doses of thiamine (up to 600 mg) and to calcium pantothenate (2 g) but B complex must always be taken along with any of the single B vitamins, as these all work together and an excess of one can upset the balance of the others. I am a great believer in vitamin C, and this is one of the most protective vitamins for the back. 1–2 g daily, taken with water, between meals, 1 gm at a time, should bring positive results. Tea, coffee, alcohol and nicotine all destroy vitamin C, and should not be taken at the same time.

For heart and circulation, fresh raw foods are

essential. The best sources of vitamin E are oils made from wheatgerm, soya bean, tung, corn, cottonseed, safflower and rice bran, followed by sunflower, peanut and cod-liver oils. Vitamin E is also present, in lesser quantities in peanut butter, shrimps, olive oil, egg yolk, muesli, brown rice, turnip greens, salmon, fresh peas, green beans, liver and tomatoes. Processing, extended cooking and deep-freezing destroys vitamin E. So does deep frying. Cold-pressing preserves the vitamin E in oils, and cold-pressed oils are always preferable. Iron pills are not compatible with vitamin E and will destroy it. Vitamin E has many valuable properties. It reduces the amount of oxygen needed by the body; helps to prevent blood clotting and dissolves clots; enables new blood-supply routes to form; strengthens and protects capillaries; heals scar tissue and creates new skin; protects diabetics; and is an anti-pollutant, like vitamin C, shielding against hardened arteries and cell damage. It also strengthens the immune system. since Americans began taking more vitamin E their heart-attack rate has dropped considerably. It is also vital for the menopause, for many of its symptoms are caused by Vitamin E deficiency, a poor diet and lack of exercise. Vitamin E will help excess sweating, which is one of the major menopause problems. Leo women often find the menopause a very difficult and stressful time. It is bad for their pride and self-image to have hot flashes and the loss of abundant fertility and womanliness of this time of life. If years of indulgent eating and lack of exercise have preceded the menopause, then there will be problems. It is wiser to prepare in advance with diet and vitamins, a health and relaxation regime, and the right frame of mind. The menopause can introduce an age of richness and wisdom; it is not the end, as some would have us believe, but only the beginning. Women are

not totally stripped of hormones but only of the ones
that are essential for conception. Age is in the mind.
You are as old as you think.

As any pet breeder will tell you, vitamin E, usually
as wheatgerm oil, is given to ensure fertility and
healthy breeding. It has the same effect on humans,
and if there has been any problem with infertility or
miscarriage – something that can cause a Leo
particular grief – then this is the prime vitamin to
take every day. That old-fashioned remedy liquid
paraffin destroys vitamin E and should never be
given to expectant mothers. Natural mixed tocoph-
erols are the best form of this vitamin, but old stock
or little-known brands should be avoided. D1-alpha
tocopherol may be the strongest version, but it is
synthetic. D-alpha tocopherol is natural. As long ago
as 1922, it was proved that this vitamin was essential
for healthy conception and pregnancy, so there is
no excuse whatsoever for the medical profession not
recommending it to their patients for such problems.
But those taking pills to prevent blood clotting should
not take high doses of vitamin E, or haemorrhage
could result.

Heart attacks as we know them are a comparatively
modern plague. When bread was stoneground, it
was full of vitamin E and other essential nutrients.
When machine milling came in at the turn of the
century, out went vitamin E and most of the wholemeal goodness, and in came heart attacks. The Victorian diet (for those who could afford it) was laden
with creams and fats and sugars, yet coronary thrombosis was unknown because their breads were solid
and heavy and packed with nutrients, their flours
rich with Nature's bounty. 'Enriched' white flour is
one of the great confidence tricks of the twentieth
century. Over a dozen nutrients are taken out of
flour, and iron is added in a form that is virtually

impossible to absorb. At one time, agene (nitrogen trichloride) was added to flour to speed up its ageing so that it could be used more quickly. This was known as 'improving' the flour! It was banned after research showed that canine hysteria could result when dogs were fed agene. When you hear scare stories about natural remedies that have been in use for many centuries, think of agene, which was in use until the 1940s; azo dyes that make children hyperactive; and the methyl mercury fungicides that used to be added to animal fodder. A family in New Mexico was seriously poisoned after cooking and eating a hog that had been dining on this treated grain. Sadly, permanent brain damage was the penalty for three of the children.

Vitamin E is the major vitamin for Leos. It protects against their most common weaknesses and keeps them fit and glowing. Symptoms of vitamin E deficiency include apathy, tiredness, short temper, muscle weakness, and lack of interest in sex, or the inability to carry through the lovemaking act as one would wish. Refined foods and the modern cooked and junk-food diet are major causes of sex becoming a turn-off. In fresh raw foods and fruits, Mother Nature's fast foods, there is all the strength and vitality of the Earth, which those who are Sun ruled need so much. 'If you want to be of the light then you must eat the light' reminds us that cooked and junk foods are dead and dark; they stress the body as it struggles to find some small measure of goodness in them and then expels the many toxins and additives which pollute it.

It is interesting that a whole league of unpleasant illnesses arises in animals that are deprived of vitamin E – including muscular dystrophy. Vitamin E-rich foods and a largely raw-food diet may well help this disease a great deal.

When the public is being wooed by those who recommend and sell polyunsaturated fats and oils, never are they told that this increases the requirement for vitamin E. For high blood pressure or any related problem, lowish doses of vitamin E should be taken for the first two weeks, 200 IU daily, then slowly increased to 600 IU daily. It's unlikely that more will be needed, but anything over 1000 IU should only be taken with a doctor or naturopath's approval. Vitamin E can be extremely helpful after heart attacks and strokes, and for artery problems and poor circulation. Taken regularly, with exercise and a healthy diet, it can keep these at bay.

I have never been an all-out supporter of the anti-cholesterol lobby. The whole matter is far more complicated. As explained earlier, flour before the present century was roughly ground and full of vitamin E, B complex, and other vital nutrients that invigorate the heart. For this reason, stoneground flour is always best. One or two free-range eggs a day can be eaten, when hens are producing them naturally without artificial intervention. Unhappy hens lay unhappy eggs. Hens go off-lay at certain times to recoup their health and strength. It isn't natural for them to be laying every single day – it exhausts them and they produce poor-calibre eggs with fewer nutrients. The same applies to hens that are crammed into tiny cages where they cannot open their wings and enjoy the sunshine. Also, many commercial eggs have their yolks coloured to give them that bright orange shade, and there can be sensitivity to this, especially in children. Free-range is best. The hens are happier, they get sunlight and they have healthier bodies and stronger bones because they can peck and dig in the dirt and grit. Cream, milk and butter are high-calorie and fill up spaces that should be left for more nourishing foods, but in *moderation*, and if there is no allergy or weight problem, I do not feel that they are dangerous. It is better to keep them for weekend treats, to maintain a healthy weight. As for meat, today it is invariably laced with hormones and antibiotics. We were never meant to eat it every day, with or without the additives it now contains. Fish is far healthier and protects the heart. So does olive oil.

Stone-Age people had an arduous time getting their meat. It might take days of careful tracking, and there could be a ferocious struggle as the finale. After all that, the meat would go bad very quickly unless it was winter time. Also, the animals pursued, baited or tracked were healthier ones: not confined to sheds, stables and racks, not force-fed hormones and other artificial products to make them fat. They were caught and eaten in a fair fight, when human survival depended upon the success of the chase. They were not shot for glory or to prove how brave and clever men are; they were not killed for the fun of it. Stone-Age people actually ate very little meat. Their staple diet was berries, nuts, roots and edible wild vegetation. They were also far more active, and when the weather was cold, they had to move about to keep warm. They couldn't slump for hours in a stuffy, centrally heated room. There is no excitement or energy expended today in the obtaining of meat or any other food; it is there in excess, and eaten in excess. We have only to open a refrigerator door to find a feast. When we have piled our plates high, we can sit in front of the television for hours and not worry about where the next meal is coming from. These differences between what Mother Nature intended for us and what we have carved out for ourselves are the main contributors towards the modern plague of heart disease, diabetes and obesity.

Cholesterol is essential for life – our own bodies produce it. Arterial wear and tear is more likely to be caused by free-radical damage, against which vitamins E and C and selenium are vital. Many quite normal bodily functions create free radicals, e.g. breathing in oxygen, which the body then changes to carbon dioxide. Nature supplied nuts and seeds with vitamin E to protect against their becoming rancid, but commercial manufacturing strips it out, thus causing the oil to become vulnerable to oxidation. This can even make us prone to cancer. Oils, fats, nuts or seeds that are not absolutely fresh should never be used. Cold-pressed oils are the only ones to use for healthy hearts and arterial systems. It is no use the labels of margarine boxes proclaiming that the contents consist of unsaturated fats, when hydrogenated fat is included in the list of ingredients.

Garlic is another treasure-trove for Leos. High in sulphur, garlic cleans out the arteries and keeps them supple, is a natural antiseptic and antibiotic, and reduces cholesterol. A glass of apple juice daily is beneficial for hypertension (unsweetened, of course, and diluted with water). It can also be helpful for hypertension to take two teaspoons of cider vinegar twice daily in a glass of water, sweetened with two teaspoons of raw, unrefined honey (unless weight is a problem – if so, the honey can be reduced or left out).

Herbal teas for Leo

Emperor's Choice, Almond Sunset, Red Zinger, Lemon Mist, Evening Peace; any teas made from fruits that have been sun dried. Apple or thyme tea for the circulation.

6

VIRGO

Before the temple of the Oracle at Delphi, the ancient Greeks – who were by no means fools – had two pieces of advice carved on the portals. One was 'Nothing in excess'. The other was 'Know thyself'.

Liz Greene, 'Sunsigns for Lovers'

The symbolism of astrology is an attempt to portray – in pictorial rather than conceptual form – the basic energies behind life and behind human beings. It's very ancient; so ancient that we don't know its origins. We know that the ancient Egyptians, Babylonians, Sumerians, Chaldeans, Indians and Chinese used it. *Liz Greene*

Virgo the Harvest Queen and Virgin: c. 23 August–c. 22 September   Element: Earth. Planetary ruler: Mercury. Physical rulership: abdomen, intestines. By polarity with Pisces: the feet.

Destiny of Virgo: to serve and heal; to withhold untoward criticism.

Herbs for Virgo: fennel, sage, balm, savory, fenugreek, valerian.

Vital vitamins and minerals for Virgo: B complex and calcium for the highly strung Virgo nervous system. Vitamin C to keep the digestive processes working smoothly. Vitamin E is valuable in preventing gastric ulcers, as is vitamin A. Nicotinamide, folic acid, pantothenic acid and thiamine (all part of the B complex) are protectors and healers of the digestive and intestinal tract. B complex should always be taken in total, never separated.

Gems for Virgo: yellow agate; tortoiseshell (see Gemini). Because of its association with Mercury (who conducted the souls of the dead to the next world in both Greek and Egyptian mythology, the latter under the name of Thoth), amethyst, a mourning colour in the West, is one of Virgo's stones. Edward the Confessor was the first British monarch to wear the amethyst as a royal emblem, and the stone was supposed to protect its wearer from evil and drunkenness – not a common Virgoan state!

The myth behind the motivation

In the days when the Great Goddess was worshipped, women were not seen as either virgins, whores or mothers. This came about as the result of hundreds of years of Christianity. Since Mary has been promoted as the ideal of womanhood, Christian women everywhere have striven to emulate her extraordinary qualities. She is a mother, a virgin, a protectress and an intermediary between humankind and God. Despite her miraculous qualities, however, Christianity put her in a humble, subservient role. God wanted to take human form and Mary was merely the vessel for this manifestation. If you think about it seriously, what did it matter to God or His Son whether the woman involved was a virgin or not? God and Christ are not obsessed with the petty preoccupations of man. It was the later Christian

Church that decided that Mary must be virginal.
However, into this assumption comes a straightforward error of translation. As John Allegro points out
in *Lost Gods*, virginity in the context of the Mother
Goddess had nothing to do with an intact hymen,
but concerned the ancient belief that a first-born child
was superior because it was fashioned from a
woman's menstrual blood when it was at its richest.
He goes on to say, 'Similarly, next in excellence to
the first-born of a young woman, a "virgin" in this
sense was the child of an older female conceiving for
the first time, just prior to menopause.' Notice how
many of the Bible's greats were born of very young,
or older mothers: John the Baptist, Isaac and Jesus
Himself.

From a misunderstanding in meaning, the whole
situation evolved into that of the Virgin Mother, a
woman who it is claimed never made love to anyone,
yet clearly had other children, for they are mentioned
in the Bible. Allegro's explanation clears up this
baffling problem. Jesus was Mary's firstborn, thus
she was a 'virgin' mother. This does not in any way
demote Mary. Indeed, she becomes more of a woman
because of it. To insist on her virginity is equivalent
to the castration of the male.

One aspect of the Great Goddess – and a very
important one – was that of the Harvest Queen.
Demeter, Ceres and Gaia are three of her names. She
was the mother of Persephone, the maiden who was
famous for being carried off by Pluto, God of the
Underworld. Persephone was also known as Kore,
which means Daughter. After the abduction,
Demeter was bereft and for nine days she would not
eat or drink or bathe as she searched for her
daughter. During her quest, the Earth withered and
faded and winter descended. Finally, Kore was
allowed to leave the Underworld, Zeus having

arranged her release; but she ate some pomegranate seeds offered to her by Pluto, which meant that she must return to his kingdom. So, for part of the year, while Kore languishes in Hades, we have winter as Demeter mourns, and when Kore returns to her mother, we have summer.

We have the same images of the Virgin Mary. She is radiant when her Son is born, when she holds Him in her arms. She mourns when He leaves her. She is the protector of mothers, she is the helper with childbirth. She is the bringer of fertility to the barren, the protectress and guardian of the young. She has a special care for young girls. She is portrayed with flowers and vines, animals and children, and has the stars encircling her head, the Moon at her feet. The Great Goddess has always been associated with the Moon, and Christianity did not abandon this connection. We have our major Christian festival at a time when pagans celebrated the rebirth of the living Sun after the winter solstice. Now we celebrate the birth of Christ, the Son, at that time. He is the Light, and every Christian is in His light. He wears a glowing halo, which was how the Sun God was portrayed in ancient times.

Virgoans still have this love and care for children. Mother Teresa is a prime example of this. The Princess Royal has three planets in Virgo. Comedian Lenny Henry, who cares deeply for Third World children, is Virgoan. Maria Montessori, who devised one of the most beneficial teaching methods for children, was a Virgoan. There are many of the benevolent aspects of the Great Goddess in every Virgoan: a desire to serve, to help and heal, to protect children, to guide the young. Unfortunately, thanks to Christian teaching, we have this very one-sided image of the Harvest Queen: she was a virgin and yet a mother. She was immaculate perfection. She never lost her temper or smacked her Child. She was purity incarnate; she never had bad or evil thoughts. She never experienced sexual feelings. She was a wife and a mother, yet a nun and a saint.

It is Virgoans who bear the brunt of this one-sided image today. Trying to live up to their own impossibly high standards is one of the Virgoan faults. They expect too much of themselves and those around them. When perfection cannot be attained, they can become irritable, complaining and difficult to live with. If they do not have some compassionate outlet, they are deeply unhappy and can turn in upon themselves.

Let us return to the days when the Great Goddess was worshipped, when every facet of woman was acknowledged and revered. She could be the Harvest Queen and devoted mother, like Demeter; or Diana, the virgin huntress, who was also the patron goddess of childbirth – which would seem somewhat odd if we did not have John Allegro's explanation about virginity. She was Hathor, the nourisher; Isis, the mystical and all-powerful, the first great White Witch (who was also an adoring mother and wife); she was Selene, the Moon Goddess, patroness of magicians. In India the Great Mother is Kali ('she who is black'), and she is portrayed with human skulls round her neck – the enemies of the gods she has slain; her blackness is the richness of the earth, not of evil. Two of her four arms are raised to give blessing to those who worship her. The many-faceted Goddess is fully acknowledged in Indian religion, while Christianity has forcibly divorced women from sex for the very reason that a fully dimensional, sexual woman is seen as a terrible threat to humankind. Why should this be? Simply because the Great Goddess religion was paramount before Christianity and everything associated with it had to be not only abandoned but destroyed, removed or concealed. Whenever woman is described, she is either evil temptress or virgin mother, either Eve who destroyed the world or Mary who saved it.

The snake was the Goddess's most sacred emblem. As I have already said, forget the Freudian associations; the snake represented wisdom and healing, rebirth and regeneration. It is carved or painted on everything associated with the Goddess. It was seen by the early Christians as her most evil representation, and the serpent of Eden represented the pagan Earth Mother religion with its fertility rites and 'debauchery'. In effect, the Eden tale is telling us that we really are the same people with the same needs, even though Christianity has struggled to pretend otherwise. Eve, of course, got the blame for it all.

The sacred fertility rites attached to the Great Goddess may sound odd to modern thinking, such as making love for the first time with a stranger at the temple, but then the act of love was not seen as a destructive, evil force, as later Christian teaching remodelled it. The feminist writers speak of the meaning of virgin as being an independent woman, for the Goddess's priestesses were called holy virgins, but if we accept the explanation given by John Allegro, then one can see why women went to the temple to dedicate themselves and their first-born to the Great Goddess in their first act of love, hoping to conceive a superior child. It was indeed the very first form of birth 'control'! Modern man has insulted the Goddess's priestesses by calling them prostitutes when they were nothing of the sort. Part of this dilemma is still suffered by Virgoan woman. Should she stay virgin? If she indulges, will it mean that she has lost her purity? In the end, she may well stay single or marry late. In fact, her powers will only be increased by motherhood and she must not be afraid

of the powerful forces within her, nor allow anyone
to make her believe that she is frightening to others.
Virgins get a bad press. They are still called 'old
maids'. Despite years of emancipation, there is still
the suggestion that women who live alone have
failed to catch a man through some fault of their own:
that they have something lacking, that the only truly
acceptable virgin is a nun.

Virgoans can be the prim, aloof women who dedicate their lives to their careers and are always
immaculately dressed in plain, serviceable clothes.
Or they can be the fertile earth mothers who lavish
their love and care for children on a massive scale.
They can be fabulously beautiful and still stay single.
Greta Garbo spoke for so many Virgoans when she
said 'I vant to be left alone.' Sophia Loren is a Virgo
and Marlene Dietrich has Virgo rising. There has
been hardly a word of scandal attached to any of
these dedicated women. Virgoan Yvonne de Carlo,
once voted the most beautiful woman in the world,
gave up her flourishing film career to nurse her sick
husband.

The fact that many Virgoans enjoy being alone
makes them ideal for the isolated life of the writer,
and very many of them are authors, and as prolific
as the other Mercury-ruled sign, Gemini. Dr Johnson,
author of the famous Dictionary, was Virgo born.
Agatha Christie, famous for her attention to detail,
was a double Virgo. The list of writers born under
this sign is endless, and includes Jane Austen (Virgo
rising), who never married; Roy Strong, with his
dedication to Elizabeth I, the Virgin Queen, who was
also born under this sign; Goethe, who wrote 'Genius
is formed in quiet'; Tolstoy, who wrote, 'All, everything that I understand, I understand only because
I love'; Edgar Rice Burroughs, whose most famous
character preferred a life of isolation in the jungle,

close to Nature; and D. H. Lawrence, who wrote earthily of passionate, overwhelming, love. Virgoan Michael Jackson, like Tarzan, prefers the private life with his animals. Authors born under the Virgo—Libra cusp include H. G. Wells (this is a cusp that can give clairvoyance, great foresight and interest in mystical and metaphysical matters), Tanith Lee, Keith Roberts, Stephen King and John Brunner. Gustav Holst, who wrote the *Planet Suite*, was born under this cusp.

Virgo can have a family, run a home and a career, and manage to give her all to each, but her highly strung nervous system suffers as a result. In her quest for perfection, she will have her home sparkling, her children reading before they start school and her career flourishing almost before other women have dressed for work!

Being born under the sign that is equated with the Virgin Mary is a hard task, and the quest for perfection can sometimes go too far and have tragic results, as with ballerina Gelsey Kirkland, who is Virgo rising. It is better to look to more ancient times, when the Great Goddess was acknowledged as the Triple Goddess. In her three major forms of Mother, Virgin and Queen of the Underworld, she was worshipped extensively in the pre-Christian world. There are few Virgo women who do not try still to be all things to all people. Beneath that cool, efficient facade there lies great passion. Think of the Earth, womb of the Great Goddess, and how serene it is until the ground quakes or a volcano erupts. Her powerful Earth forces can be used extensively for the good of humankind. The 'old maid' is perhaps the saddest, most restricted type of Virgoan. She has come to a halt too early, before her beautiful flowering. She is Demeter in winter and will never know spring.

Physically, Virgoans usually have deep blue eyes,

but sometimes they have dark brown eyes not unlike those of Scorpio, but without the piercing Scorpio gaze. The Mercurial chin is small and pointed (Anita Dobson, Angie in *EastEnders* is Virgo rising). They are neat and tidy, immaculately turned out, not a hair out of place, their colour scheme perfectly coordinated, their shoes never scuffed or worn, their hands spotless and manicured. They often favour beautifully cut suits or dresses, and the women have neat, attractive feet clad in smart court shoes. Their jewellery is always tasteful, never flashy. The women have the Earth Mother contours – a good bust, slender waist and curvaceous hips, with shapely legs – but those who have worn themselves to a standstill with nervous tension will be thin and wiry. Often the women have long and very beautiful nails and they use their hands expressively. Virgoans can possess an earthy sexual attractiveness and great charisma. Think of Richard Gere; Racquel Welch; Margaret Lockwood; Sean Connery; Charles Boyer. Their hair colouring is very dark brown, its texture silky and fine, and their eyebrows are highly arched; they may have rather thin but well shaped lips. Their noses are long and straight (sometimes very long, as with Francis I and Edith Sitwell). Build is small to medium, and the overall impression of the average Virgoan is one of neatness, tastefulness and self-control. They have good bone structure, like the other Earth signs, Taurus and Capricorn. The Virgo sense of humour is sharp, Mercurial and fast, but always clean. Lenny Henry is a prime example; his three planets in Leo and Sagittarius rising giving him the extroversion of those signs. Harry Secombe is also born under Virgo, but does not have the Virgo physique!

The Virgo child

Lively. Talkative. Inquisitive. Restless. Home-loving. Sensitive. Nervous. All these apply to the Virgoan child, who is a late developer emotionally but not mentally, yet has a very grown-up facade. Interested in books from the first, a mine of information as time goes on, and intrigued by everything and everyone; some writing ability may show quite early. (It started at the age of six for this author.) Far too modest, far too retiring and shy, Virgoan children need to be encouraged, drawn out of their shells, praised and loved and indulged at times. They have inborn self-discipline and level-headedness, so rarely go astray. Mercury-ruled, like Gemini, they must be taught how to rest and relax, so they don't burn themselves out. They have marvellous powers of recuperation, however (like the Earth that rules them), and will spring back quickly. They will be interested in healthy eating and may insist on becoming vegetarian. If they do, they should be given informative books on the subject so that they know what they should be eating and won't go short of nourishment. They need the B vitamin complex for their digestive systems and delicate intestinal tract. Nicotinamide (niacin) is in yeast extract, dried brewer's yeast, wheat bran, pig's liver, chicken, soya flour, meat and oily fish, wheat grains, cheese, dried fruits, wholemeal bread and brown rice, oatflakes and eggs. Folic acid is in brewer's yeast, soya flour, wheatgerm, wheat bran, fresh nuts, pig's liver and kidney, green-leaved vegetables, pulses, oatflakes, roasted nuts, wheat grains, wholemeal bread, citrus fruits, eggs, unpolished brown rice, oily fish, bananas, cheese, root vegetables, potatoes, dried fruits, meats and milk.

Pantothenic acid is in yeast, pig's liver, yeast

extract, pig kidney, fresh nuts, wheat bran, wheat-germ, roasted nuts, soya flour, meats, poultry, oatflakes, pulses, dried fruits, maize, unpolished brown rice, wholemeal bread, cheese, yoghourt, fruits, green-leaved and root vegetables. If the intestinal bacteria are flourishing, then the B vitamins can be produced by the body. If antibiotics have been given, then the intestinal flora will be under threat and will need plenty of live yoghourt, brewer's yeast, olive oil, and multivitamins – especially B complex – so that they can recreate themselves. Antibiotics kill off all the healthy bacteria alone with the unhealthy: not a very nice state of affairs at all. It means that the body is vulnerable to infection and disease.

Usually the Virgo child will accept a sensible explanation for why she or he may have to do something, unlike the Aries child, who will argue, and the Taurus child, who will stubbornly resist. Once started on an interest, they will pursue it until they have drained every shred of information that they can, displaying a depth of knowledge that can be amazing. They have a more long-lasting approach than Gemini, who flits from novelty to novelty. As a rule, they keep their interests for life, and love in-depth analysis and reflection.

Between late 1962 and 1968 the Virgoan generation was born. That is, children who had a powerful Uranus/Pluto conjunction in Virgo. This generation has been faced with life or death situations. For some, this may mean depression that they can't shake off, a feeling of such desperation that they even contemplate suicide; or it may simply be the eagerness to fling themselves into close confrontation with death. A few will, sadly, achieve this; others will survive, stronger and fitter. This generation has needed extra care and attention, but those lucky enough to have caring parents will have got through without serious mishap. Those with the sort of strong birthchart that can withstand such an inflammatory conjunction will have survived, especially if they have talent, too. Many are skilled with computers and were born for the computer age. Others have suffered all the problems of unemployment (Virgo rules employment). However, none of this is forced upon us. We all choose our own destinies and the problems that we must encounter. In the East, this is called the wheel of Karma, but it has just as much relevance to us here in the West. Of course, when we find out that this process is more painful and difficult than we could ever have imagined, we feel different; but then if we didn't feel like this, it would not be the lesson that we need.

The best of these Uranus/Pluto conjunction children will be very special for mankind and will help us through the age to come. The young Virgo generation now in evidence is sensible, organised, hard-working and law-abiding. Old heads on young shoulders aptly describes them – and how different they are from their parents, the Neptune in Libra generation with their long hair, flowered robes, liberality and dedication to Love and Peace!

If a child born in these years has driven you mad with behaviour that was baffling and beyond your comprehension, with moods and depressions, and dabbling in drugs and other hallucinogenics, then feel compassion for them. The lesson they have to learn is hard – too hard for some. They need all the help we can give them. Remember that they are our future.

Health

Being Earth-ruled gives Virgoans an extra resilience. They can bounce back after setbacks that would finish others. Most of their problems are of nervous origin, for although they are famous as the sign that eats wisely and is interested in healthy diets, the nervous strain they suffer can lead them to cigarettes. Those who smoke thirty cigarettes a day are getting as much plutonium as they would from three hundred X-rays a year! Added to that, every cigarette uses up 30 mg of vitamin C, the vitamin that protects against pollution, infection and disease. No wonder smoking takes its toll! It is also incriminated in cancer of the cervix, for the tobacco toxins permeate the entire body, not just the lungs. Don't do it, Virgo! If you smoke for relaxation, remember that there is no place more relaxed than an early grave.

There are some excellent detoxification diets around today and they will help Virgoans to keep their delicate stomachs in good shape. An excessively acid body encourages cravings for tea, coffee, cigarettes, alcohol and meat. A diet of sprouted seeds, vegetables, salads and mineral water keeps the body on the right side of alkalinity so that the torment of cravings can be beaten. Believe me, I know it's not easy conquering cravings. I was once a sugar addict, a chocolate addict . . . I still succumb to tea, especially Earl Grey, which is now my only dietary weakness. I have beaten all the others, and anyone can do the same. The feeling of achievement is marvellous, and far exceeds whatever enjoyment you imagined your habit was giving you. Tea, coffee and cola drinks can inhibit iron absorption. Tobacco may affect eye focus and length of sight. Female Virgoans can suffer difficult and painful periods and prolonged premenstrual tension because of their highly strung systems, and an acidic, addictive body will only make these worse.

If smoking were introduced for the first time now, there would be horror at the notion of people waving around burning, smoking sticks in their hands. It would be called irresponsible, dangerous, socio-pathic. It is, of course, all of these things – and smokers cannot imagine how nasty it smells to nonsmokers.

The strain of struggling to be perfect is a hefty burden, but if Virgoans pay for it with their health, then they have proved beyond all doubt that they are not perfect, haven't they?

Relaxation has enormous benefits for those who are Mercury ruled. Autohypnosis can be learned in five or six sessions and gives a cocoon of soothing protection that can be wrapped around the body whenever the need arises. The tortured Virgoan nerves tend to affect their digestions, and nervous stomachs, indigestion, irritable bowel syndrome, heartburn and stomach upsets can hound them if they do not take protective steps with diet and relax-ation. Simple yoga breathing, either through the nose or alternate nostrils, will benefit them, as will walking or cycling whenever they feel jittery and tangled up. If nails are bitten because of excess tension, a herbal tranquilliser such as Quiet Life or Kalms should be taken when that knot of tension begins in the stomach. Nail biting sets up a circle of tension through arms, neck, shoulders and head which can lead to headaches and permanent soreness in the shoulder area. At regular intervals, especially if sitting at a desk, Virgoans should hunch the shoul-ders up to the ears three or four times and let them flop down. Circling the shoulders eases pins and needles in hands and arms. Circling the head can actually stop a headache forming. To interrupt a headache before it gets a hold at the first signs of pain, drop the head on the chest and move it slowly up to the left shoulder, then drop it back to the chest in a rolling movement. Do the same towards the right shoulder and repeat five or six times.

Stretching exercises are also wonderful for tension but need to be done two or three times a week for regular benefit. A simple yoga total relaxation exercise is alternate-nostril breathing. This will balance the positive and negative body energies. Sitting straight backed, breathe in through the right nostril, then press the thumb over the right nostril, hold the breath for a moment, then breathe out through the left nostril. With the little finger of the right hand, press shut the left nostril and breathe in through the right nostril. Repeat. This may be speeded up after a time, for about thirty in-out breaths without a momentary pause in between, then slowed down. The eventual aim for those who wish to become adept is one breath every three minutes, but the relaxation benefits can be enjoyed long before this. Always breathe in through the right nostril and out through the left. There are other relaxation exercises with a yoga base, but this is one of the most effective.

Calcium is a soother, and one or two tablets at night with hot milk can help insomnia. Quiet Life herbal tranquillisers are invaluable. They can be taken during the day and last thing at night to take off that extra painful edge caused by highly strung nerves. The planet Mercury brings many benefits – intense creativity, a sharp mind, an excellent memory, a fund of knowledge and lively energy – but it is hard for Virgoans to appreciate these when they are hunched up, taut and tangled, biting their nails or smoking furiously and dominated by a jangling nervous system and unreliable digestion! Mercury energy comes in great rushes, rather like

electrical overload. Virgoans should think of themselves as conductors, and realise that they must be
properly insulated at all times, or they will short-
circuit or frizzle to a crisp from overload.

The alkaline diet is recommended (there is a list of
alkaline and acid foods at the back of this book), with
raw vegetables and fruits, plain live yoghourt (very
soothing for unreliable digestive systems as it is
predigested and full of the healthy bacteria that keeps
the intestines flourishing), chamomile tea, and the
herb valerian, which is a nerve relaxant. B complex,
in B50 or B100 dosage should be taken daily (an extra
one or two for those under great stress). Brewer's
yeast is a rich source of the B vitamins and of RNA
and DNA. It makes hair healthy and also contains
chromium to help keep the blood sugar even, so that
cravings can be conquered.

The great argument against a diet of cooked food
is the high vitamin losses that are a direct result of
the heating process. For instance, 30–50 per cent of
vitamin C is lost during boiling after peeling; 20–40
per cent after boiling when unpeeled; 20–40 per cent
when baked, roasted or steamed. Chips have lost
25–35 per cent of their vitamin C. People who smoke,
and live on cooked food, will be desperately short of
C. The first signs of this is bleeding, sore or swollen
gums. This is the early gingivitis that will turn into
pyorrhoea, the bone loss due to bacterial inflammation. The next stage is tooth loss. Vitamin C, when
taken in its complete complex, along with bioflavonoids (also known as rutin and vitamin P), plus a
largely raw-food diet can help to prevent this.
Remember that convenience foods are made for the
convenience of the manufacturer, not for the
consumer! They are cheaper and easier to make, they
can be compressed and dried and reduced in size so
that they are cheaper and easier to transport; they

don't need expensive contents (i.e. real, nutritive food!) and they can be advertised with more zing. Frequently, a pointer to watch for is the brightly coloured, lively, jolly advert, the vibrant hard-sell that denotes the presence of processed, denatured food.

Busy working parents may argue that they find convenience foods a boon, but it only takes seconds to fill dishes with fresh fruit, nuts, seeds and scrubbed raw vegetables when your children arrive home from school. These dishes can be put ready in the fridge, in airtight bowls to stop vitamin leakage. Have you ever read the list of ingredients in commercial processed food? They are horrifying. How could anyone feed these to adults, let alone children? These are not only dead foods but dead chemicals. I call these processed horrors, foods from the Dead Zone. Dead foods cannot support healthy, vigorous life.

Sugar destroys vitamin B in the body and thus affects the nervous system. It irritates stomach ulcers. It also causes the roller-coaster of excessively high and excessively low blood sugar, which can cause irritability, tension, headaches, temper explosions and moodiness. One teaspoon of sugar a day is one teaspoon too many. There is already too much added to canned foods, commercial foods, sauces and ketchups without adding any more. There are seven teaspoons of sugar in a can of cola! This blast of destructive poison is more than any pancreas can stand and will only remove Virgoans further from the calmer, more relaxed state that they crave. They should nibble sunflower seeds if they yearn for sugar or a cigarette – these are alakaline and will help to fight cravings – and eat fresh fruit when they long for something exciting. There are many unusual and exotic fruits available now, such as mangoes or Chinese gooseberries or lychees, which are a pleasure to eat, unlike the sugary sweet that makes you desperate for another and another and another. . . .

The true Virgoan does not have a weight problem, but those with one of the 'fat' signs on their ascendant, Libra, for example, may, in their impatience for results, try a very low-calorie diet. Having tried them myself, I cannot recommend them. In the 1970s, when doctors told us that exercise could not help weight loss, women went onto starvation diets, well below 1000 calories, believing that this was the only way to lose pounds. I was one of them. As a direct result, I have had various health problems over the years, including water retention and my nerves in tatters. Makers may claim that everything needed for health is in their diet powder, but how do they know everything that is needed for health? The discovery of vitamins is comparatively modern. Much is still unknown. American and Russian experts recommend far higher doses than British experts. We are finding out new things all the time about nutrition. It is obviously impossible for any powder to contain everything needed for health. For a start, these powders contain no fresh raw food, no fibre, nothing for the teeth to chew on and no living enzymes.

The only way to lose weight, unwelcome though this knowledge can be, is by regular exercise, a fresh raw-food diet, cutting out white sugars, white flour, sweets and chocolate, alcohol and sugary drinks and taking a sensible amount of food supplements in the form of multivitamins, vitamin C and B complex.

Herbal teas for Virgo

Peppermint, spearmint, mint and fennel for stomach disorders; Lemon Mist; chamomile, valerian and balm for the nervous system. Evening Peace by Jill Davies – or any herbal tea containing hops to help sleeplessness. For a tense and nervous stomach: balm and marjoram.

7

LIBRA

> Man is an intrinsic part of Nature. The
> same life processes which bring forth
> plant or animal also take place in man.
> Plant, bird, beast and man are alike
> dependent for existence upon the Sun,
> the Earth, the air, the rain – upon the
> interaction of the four elements, Fire,
> Earth, Air and Water. *Joan Hodgson*

Libra, Lady of Love and Justice: c. 23 September–
c. 23 October   Planetary ruler: Venus. Element:
Air. Physical rulership: the kidneys, lower back and
renal system. By polarity with Aries: the head.

Destiny of Libra: to spread light and sweetness,
soothing troubles. Most difficult thing to do: face
unjust anger.

Herbs for Libra: dandelion, parsley, pennyroyal,
yarrow. Walnuts and aduki beans are recommended
by the Chinese for the kidneys: a few walnuts daily;
one ounce of aduki beans daily.

Vital vitamins and minerals for Libra: vitamin C for a
healthy back, bladder and renal system; vitamin A to
help fight infection in this area. Chromium helps to
keep blood sugar level, and is obtainable alone or in
fortified brewer's yeast.

Gems for Libra: emerald, sapphire, aventurine, nephrite, jade. Supernatural qualities have been associated
with jade for many centuries, particularly by the
Mayans and Libra-ruled Egyptians, who carved

scarabs out of it. In prehistoric days, axe heads and knives were fashioned from it, which does not seem to fit the Venusian characteristics until one remembers that the Goddess of Love was also the Goddess of War. The Chinese associate jade with the five major virtues of wisdom, mercy, modesty, courage and justice. China, too, is ruled by Libra. The metal for this sign is copper. Looking glasses are Venus ruled and were originally made from copper. Copper turns green, and green is Venus's colour.

The myth behind the motivation

Maat was the Egyptian Goddess of Justice, Truth and cosmic harmony. She was the daughter of Re, the Sun God of Heliopolis. Her symbol is an ostrich feather (ostriches hide their heads in the sand, and our own modern statue of Justice is blindfold). Egyptian judges wore a representation of Maat when administering the law. The Pharaohs were called 'beloved of Maat' and enjoyed a close relationship with the goddess. Without the ministrations of Maat, no one could enter the next world, for it was she whose scales were used to weigh the hearts of the dead. The heart was put on one side of the scales and her feather on the other. A heavy heart would not pass the test, and its owner would be tied to the wheel of reincarnation until the heart was sufficiently light when weighed again in the future.

The Greek Goddess of Law and Justice was Athena, who sprang fully armed from her father's head. The Greeks had no problem in accepting a fully independent female who could think and speak for herself, and was at ease in a man's world without losing any of her femininity. In the West, women who display Athena's autonomy, shrewdness, self-sufficiency, wisdom and judgment are all too frequently called aggressive, ruthless or hard. Female Librans who wish to take their place as lawyers, barristers and company heads should not allow anyone to dissuade them. Because Librans are Venus-ruled, this sign can be very beautiful physically, dimpled and pretty, curvaceous and feminine visually – but they have minds capable of cool logic and excellent judgment. Eye colouring will be similar to Venus-ruled Taurus: greeny-blue, blue, greyish-green or olive (Athena's gift to her people was the olive tree). Almond-shaped eyes are very much a feature of Libra, and they can be deep set. Hair colouring is usually fair or light brown, its texture fine, silky and often curly. Complexions are creamy fair, and dimples are virtually obligatory for the Venus-ruled. Hands will be small and shapely, figure curvy and generous, legs beautiful, noses snub, mouths will have cupid's bows. Voices are velvet-toned, smooth and honeyed (Anna Ford, and many of the honey-voiced singers, such as Cliff Richard, Johnny Mathis, Rita Hayworth, Barbara Dickinson and Bryan Ferry are Librans). George Gershwin, America's greatest musician, was Libran.

Generally, Librans are more chatty and outgoing than Taureans, which is one way of identifying them because they can look very much alike.

Not surprisingly, nearly all of the great screen goddesses are or were Venus-ruled, or have Venus strongly in their charts. It can be difficult for a man who sees such a sensual vision to accept that there is a shrewd and logical mind behind it, and this is one of the problems that Libran women have to face. They may deliberately attempt to make themselves look plain if they wish to enter the law, and some may even go so far as to make no effort to keep their shape, for fat is a welcome protection against all the unwarranted attention that being physically attractive brings.

Athena was too independent, too autonomous, denying her femininity for the sake of excelling in the male world; but if we consider her birth, we can see why. Her mother was Metis, the wisest of the exalted ones, and Zeus, with typical male ego, feared that their expected child would outflank him in every way. His solution was to devour the pregnant Metis. However, this was not the end of Athena. When she was ready to be born, she sprang fully armed from the head of her father, and grew without the gentle and feminine support of her mother. She was one of the famed virgin goddesses of the ancient world (see Cancer and Virgo for more details). Originally her symbol was the snake, with which she is portrayed, and she was also called 'the owl-eyed' so was probably represented in owl form in earliest times. The snake represents wisdom and healing, and Athena was also Minerva Medica, Goddess of Physicians. The owl, a mysterious creature of the night, represents the sagacity and female intuition that Athena inherited from her mother. She was also bearer of the aegis, the legendary shield on which she affixed the head of Medusa, which could turn those who looked upon it to stone.

A wonderful subject for horror stories, the Medusa's head, writhing with snakes, was far from being the repellent weapon of death that lurid imagination has made it. The snakes are the symbol of wisdom and healing, remember; they represent the deepest, most mysterious aspects of feminine wisdom; they were sacred to the Great Goddess, who was worshipped in the deepest, darkest caves. Snakes sprang from the Earth that was the Goddess herself and were used in her most sacred rites. The advancing, male-dominated Christianity feared and loathed everything that was related to the Great Mother (see Cancer). Originally, those who stared into the face of the Medusa were endowed with the wisdom of Metis. Finally, after male (Christian) tampering with the legend, it was said that they were turned to stone. The change was made so that no one would realise how beneficial feminine gifts were, these now being viewed as fiendish, dangerous things that led men into terrible temptation and destroyed their souls. The last thing that the early Christian Fathers wanted was a return to the days when womankind was revered and had an equal share in all things. However, by censoring the energies and mysteries of womankind and spreading lies about her dangerous, destructive sexuality, an inharmonious, unbalanced world was created – which is what we have had for much of the last two thousand years.

Very conscious of such disharmony, Librans are greatly moved by injustice. They can enjoy a fine vision of a love and peace-filled world and work towards it in a way unequalled by other signs. Mahatma Gandhi, Bob Geldof, Lech Walesa, Winnie Mandela and Bishop Desmond Tutu are all Librans. Princess Anne has Libra on the ascendant, as did Winston Churchill; and John Lennon has left us his songs of love for inspiration. Princess Diana has Libra on the midheaven, and helped by her Cancerian Moonchild sun sign, cares deeply for children and the young, spreading light and love wherever she goes. Injustice, especially where it concerns the young, rouses Libra's full involvement. They will work unceasingly in such a cause.

It is those Librans who do not heed the call of Metis who idle away their lives in self-indulgence and empty pleasures, frittering time and money without heed for the needs of others, beset by a torpor that shackles them . . . almost as if turned to stone.

Athena (also known as Minerva) could bestow the gift of prophecy and endow long life. She was the first person to build a ship, and she watched over the Argonauts on their famous voyage. She had extraordinary blue eyes and because of this was given the name of Glaucopis. She presided over markets and she taught humankind how to manage the horse, for which she was given the name Minerva Hippea. She also invented the flute. In ancient times, love and war usually featured together and thus she was also Goddess of War along with the arts. Zeus, her father, infamous for his egocentric love affairs and his habit of throwing thunderbolts when he was feeling off colour, gave his daughter permission to throw thunderbolts too, but she declined, being wiser than he. A very versatile woman. . . .

Libra is an artistic sign, a lover of beauty, and yet it has one of the plainest symbols, the scales. I prefer to think of Libra as Lady of Love and Justice. There are few Librans who are not moved by unfairness, and although they prefer a peaceful life and enjoy all the good things available, they can be tigerish in the defence of those in need. Their way is one of love, peace and harmony, Gandhi being the prime example of this, and they are renowned for weighing up every aspect of a subject or problem, perhaps to the point of excessive dithering when they can't make up their minds. They may think they know what they want – until someone gives them an alternative, and then problems really set in. Their natural gift for balance and harmony can aid them greatly with selection (Dr Bach of 'Flower Remedy' fame was born under this sign), and if they have other dynamic signs in their birthchart they can be superb at doing things in the fairest possible way. Like Maat, who had the unenviable task of deciding who was fit to pass into the next world, Librans can make decisions that others would find impossible. They are shrewd, perceptive, intuitive, and cool-headed – but their hearts are warm.

Mrs Thatcher is Libra with dynamic Scorpio rising and Mars conjunct her sun sign to give her endless energy.

We see in her a modern Athena. She has the power to hurl the thunderbolts of Zeus, and will do it if there is no alternative, yet she much prefers the peaceful way. She has the duty of meting out justice (meting comes from Metis) with a limited fund of money when there are so many just and deserving causes. When she takes the reins into her hands (as Minerva Hippea) she inevitably achieves success. Mrs Thatcher, like Athena, is proud of her origins, proud of being her father's daughter.

Athena was celibate, but this applies to few Librans for they are happiest in partnership, eager to make up for what Athena lacked. A man without a woman or a woman without a man causes an imbalance. They have a deep need for a close, affectionate and fulfilling relationship – possibly because the memory of Athena's lonely stance is still fresh in their subconscious minds. They cannot bear aggravation, arguments and insults, and will let people walk over them at times rather than summon the courage required to put a stop to it. The offering of the olive branch began with Athena, and this can be an honourable gesture, or the feeblest submission. The Librans who would never expect others to give in to them every time are far too willing to do this themselves.

The Libra child

The Libran baby will be a cuddly, loving, affectionate
and dimpled bundle. As soon as they can manage it,
they should be given paper and felt tips, paints and
pencils, wrapped in a large bib and seated on a plastic
sheet covered with paper; they will be blissful. They
will notice flowers and birds and butterflies before
other children; they will adore animals and love
cuddling furry creatures. Unfortunately, they have
one of the sweetest tooths of the zodiac, and to keep
them healthy and slim, they should be breast-fed
and refined sugar, honey and sweetened fruit juices
should not come their way. Parents can give them
rosy apples and bright orange carrot sticks when they
are hungry between meals . . . they will love the
colours of them. They can have fresh fruit for
puddings, too. If they take their lunch to school, they
should have wholemeal bread, low-calorie cheeses,
tomatoes, eggs and two types of brightly coloured
fruit. Sausages, preserved meat, meat pies and
pasties, chips, fried foods and fatty crisps are
anathema for Librans, who will rapidly put on weight
as they have little affinity for exercise. (If they have
Mars rising they will be more energetic, and then
will need higher calorie foods, of course.) Sweets and
sugary puddings are very seductive; they upset the
appetite, increasing hunger and building a carousel
of low and high blood sugar that will end with a
permanent weight problem and possibly pancreatic
damage and the beginnings of diabetes.

Artificially coloured food and drinks may attract
the colour-loving Libran, but these are to be avoided.
Parents should teach them that natural is best, and
tell them about the Earth spirits who help to grow
natural foods; they will love such tales. They will
readily understand that there are no Earth spirits

in factories helping to produce artificial, processed foods, and that there is no natural magic in such false foods.

They will like to hear the tale of Metis and Athena, and should be encouraged to love wild life and conservation, and to help others. Librans can be led astray when they are young, so their companions have to be chosen carefully; they must be taught wisdom and a little caution, without being dissuaded from trusting others.

They need harmony more than most; angry and bitter exchanges will upset them deeply. If they get depressed, they can be cheered with a nature walk or stories about faeries – happy tales with a happy ending. They will love romantic stories and films as they grow older. Many romantic novelists are born under this sign, helping to balance the scales of the world against all the violence and bloodshed. Beautiful things raise the Libran spirits, and books can supply an unending fund of colour pictures. Fashion and jewellery, drama, the theatre, cinema, animals, costume exhibitions, paintings and art in all its forms will absorb their interest, and they also need to meet friends regularly for they mix easily and need plenty of social contact.

Being Air-ruled, like Gemini and Aquarius, at times they may have trouble sleeping and make themselves so excited that they feel sick with nerves. Chamomile tea will help that. It has a sweet scent, not unlike new-mown hay, and soothes the nerves. One herbal sleeping pill at night should take the edge off the excess nervousness, and this is far better than getting into poor sleeping habits and not being able to wake in time for school.

Libran children should have alarm clocks as soon as they are capable of using them, and be allowed to get themselves up in the morning. This will prevent what might turn into years of sleepy mornings when parents try to rouse them and fail. If they are encouraged to put out their clothes the night before, they won't spend an hour deciding what to wear. Simple routines can obviate the need for tense moments of decision: socks first, or underwear? They like to be involved in everything that concerns the family and can feel excluded if they aren't consulted on day-to-day matters. Family meetings are a good idea if there is at least one Libran in the family, at a regular time, when everything can be discussed and debated. They will love this and it will hone their shrewd minds in readiness for the adult world.

It is never wise to pamper children, to think that life will be tough enough when they leave home so they should be shielded while in your care. The adult world will seem all the harsher if they have never been allowed to make a decision, care for themselves and their parents, or take their part in the running of the home. Libran children of both sexes will enjoy baking and preparing cakes and buns for family teas. Now is the time for them to learn about wholemeal flour and raw brown sugar, and the advantages of dried fruit or grated carrots as a sweetener. They should be encouraged to prepare salads, too, for this can be done very artistically with brightly coloured and interesting ingredients. If they realise from an early age that salads aren't just a lettuce leaf and a slice of tomato, then they will make them a part of their daily diet, thus establishing a healthy routine. The fibre in salads and vegetables will help to keep them slim, and the minerals and vitamins they contain will help to prevent the sweet cravings that Librans suffer. An important lesson is that the more enticingly a food or drink is promoted, packaged and labelled, the less natural it is likely to be.

Health

Librans adore French cooking, expensive chocolates and sweet puddings, buttery biscuits and sweet wines, and although those with a strong Mars influence in their charts are likely to be sporty and energetic, the majority dislike making the extra effort that exercise needs. Libran comedian Ronnie Barker has retired early with high blood pressure, yet he still says that he won't take exercise even though he has always been overweight. Elizabeth Taylor and Dolly Parton (both Libra rising) have fought a long battle with excess fat. It is far better to be realistic about this and grapple with it as soon as possible, for it won't go away. Every high-calorie food and drink beloved by Librans will add to their weight problem. That old adage: 'a moment in the mouth and a lifetime on the hips' is all too sadly true for this sign. Librans should not waste time feeling sorry for themselves and slumping into self-pity that will encourage them to reach for the chocolates. If they do, then they will never win the battle. Some people can eat heartily and never put on weight, but Librans are not among them.

Fortunately, there are many interesting diets available today. I do not include the very low-calorie ones, for these provoke more trouble than they are worth. The humble oat is a great friend, for it will keep the blood sugar level and lend stamina. The Scots were fit and vigorous on their old-time diet of porridge oats and oatcakes. When they began to smoke, and eat white sugar and an excess of meat, they ushered in ill health on a plate and now have the highest heart-attack rate. Of course, adding sugar and cream to oats makes them high calorie. Adding cinnamon, a little sea salt, a spoonful of mineral-rich black molasses, or a small sprinkling of dark brown sugar and a little skimmed milk, makes a filling, low-calorie meal that will keep off hunger pangs for hours. Anyone feeling hungry within two or three hours of this dish, knows for sure that he or she is just being greedy.

Nathan Pritikin's diet and health books are highly recommended. He has reversed the ill health even of elderly people who were practically immobile. He has got octogenarians running every day – and winning races. Of course, it is entirely up to Librans if they want to be chair or bedridden with arthritis, creaking joints and high blood pressure at a comparatively early age. We all have freedom of choice. But if they want to stay fit, active and independent, then they must tackle their sweet tooth and conquer it. It doesn't mean that they can't indulge now and again. What it does mean is that they will enjoy their favourite foods even more when they are eaten less regularly. They may even taste them properly for the first time! If they can remind themselves about balance in all things, then this will help their willpower. Eating fattening foods at every meal is not keeping a balance, is it? Healthy eating and exercise during the week will enable them to relax a little at the weekend (but for those who overdo it, the Monday blues will hit hard. The low-spirited feeling is frequently due to low blood sugar after a weekend of mad indulgence. When they are eaten less often, it is possible to see what effect sweet foods have on blood-sugar levels and realise that they cause tiredness, irritability and sometimes depression, too.)

Those who read about honey and believe that it is low-calorie, or superior to sugar in every way, have been misled. Like all natural foods, it comes with its own fibre – the waxy honeycomb debris with its sprinkling of pollen and propolis. However, most honeys are refined, which means that they have been heated in their country of origin to make them malleable, and then added to other honeys and probably heated again. Now they can display a nicely reassuring label saying 'Pure Honey', but heat destroys much of the goodness, and what remains is a high-sugar, high-calorie food with little goodness. It has exactly the same effect on the pancreas as white sugar. One spoonful a day if not overweight is the maximum I would recommend, and this must be from the unrefined comb so that the honey can be chewed instead of swallowed like a drink. Even if the honey *is* unrefined and fresh from the comb, one would still need to eat pounds of it to get the daily requirement of vitamins and minerals, and this is plainly impractical. Beekeepers eat the unheated, hand-collected dregs of the comb with all its nourishing pollen, propolis and fibre, which is why they have such a good health record. They are also likely to be more active than the average, because keeping bees is arduous, demanding work, so they have the incentive to keep fit.

What applies to honey also applies to fruit juices. Try and eat sixteen pounds of apples or oranges at one sitting! Even if this were feasible, there would be an uncomfortable feeling of fullness and possibly an upset stomach. Mother Nature supplies her sweet stuffs with lots of fibre, the idea being that those who want a little of the fructose, or fruit sugar, will have to munch through mouthfuls of high-fibre, nutritious fruit to gain it. Gulping down the juice without the fibre is like giving the pancreas a kick. It is better to stick to the whole fruit, or water the juice half and half. Best of all, press it at home, fresh each time and include all the pith of oranges (but not the skins, for they are now coated with chemicals to make them shiny) and all the core and skins of apples – after scrubbing them well in water and one teaspoon of vinegar. The pips of apples contain eight times more iodine than the rest, and iodine is essential for a healthy thyroid. Underactive thyroids encourage weight gains.

The kidneys and the lumbar region are the weak spots for Librans, and these must always be protected. Librans should never sit in draughts or in a deckchair, which will leave their backs cold, and always keep their feet warm and dry, for chilled feet can bring on cystitis. Eating a few walnuts daily helps to maintain healthy kidneys. Drinking plenty of mineral or spring water (preferably the low-sodium variety like Volvo) flushes out the renal system. Strong tea and coffee should be avoided, as they overstimulate the kidneys and dehydrate the body. Antibiotics are not recommended as a cure for cystitis, because they leave the body in a weakened condition and encourage more attacks. (I speak from experience.) Drinking as much non-tap water as possible is first on the list of priorities, along with cutting out all sugar; but drinking to the point of discomfort puts further stress on the kidneys and can result in waterlogging. Vitamin C will help to fight the poisons, and the dosage of this should be increased the moment that symptoms appear. The system should be made as alkaline as possible by eating plenty of citrus fruits (these turn alkaline in the body) and salads. Plain live yoghourt will help to fight off the attack, as will raw fresh vegetables. There is an excellent anticystitis diet in *Food on Your Plate* (see bibliography). Thorough cleansing of the area and emptying of the bladder after sexual intercourse is one of the regular preventives. Others are to avoid scented soaps and bath foams; rinse the area thoroughly using cold water for the final rinse; and to dab on a little Tiki vitamin E oil externally, especially if there is any abrasion.

The fruit fast might exacerbate the symptoms for a while, but this will be the result of the body getting rid of its toxins and is a common reaction when nature cures are undertaken. It will help to rest, keep warm, drink plenty of water and cut out more solid foods temporarily. Cats know what is best for them when they are feeling off colour. They shun food, drink more water and sleep. Theirs is a good example, for they are wiser about these things than we are. We are largely made of water (in emergencies, sea water has been used as a 'blood' transfusion), and water has a valuable part to play in healing us.

Herbal teas for Libra

Rose. Chamomile to soothe and restore. Verbena (vervain) for the kidneys and associated problems; Morning Starter, Evening Peace and China Light by Jill Davies. Dandelion coffee (what keeps the liver healthy helps to keep the kidneys healthy). For inflammation of kidneys and bladder: strawberry or cherry tea, freshly made if possible.

8

SCORPIO

Leaving fate on one side for the
moment, a little more self reflection –
with the aid of an astrological
microscope – would improve all our
relationships by leaps and bounds.
Penny Thornton

The origins of astrology are shrouded in
superstition. This is true as well for
chemistry, medicine, and astronomy, to
mention only three.   *Carl Sagan*

Scorpio the Scorpion: c. 24 October–c. 21 November
Planetary rulers: Pluto and Mars. Element: Water.
Physical rulership: reproductive organs, bladder, and
the 'underworld' of the body, the rectum and prostate (in males). By polarity with Taurus: the throat.

Destiny of Scorpio: to abandon all thoughts of revenge,
both mentally and physically. To admit that they can
sometimes be fallible.

Herbs for Scorpio: sweet basil; tarragon; hops; nettles;
wild arrach. Agnus Castus for female disorders.

Vital vitamins and minerals for Scorpio: vitamin E and
zinc for the reproductive system. B complex for the
ovaries. For prostate problems: oil of evening primrose, and safflower oil daily, plus 20 mg zinc,
sunflower seeds and pollen. Chelated magnesium for
potency problems. See Taurus for throat treatment.

Gems for Scorpio: red tourmaline. In Christian art, red

symbolised the Holy Spirit, divine love and royalty.
It could also mean blood, battle and violence. Tourmaline has unusual electro-magnetic properties.

The myth behind the motivation

The sign Scorpio has had a very bad press, having
become synonymous with revenge, malice and
promiscuous sexuality, and while it is true that negative members of this sign can exhibit all this, the
large majority do not. Long forgotten are the earliest
representations of the Scorpion as nourisher, protective mother and guardian of the dead. The Egyptians
worshipped a scorpion goddess, Selket. The Greeks
called her Selkis. While the Great God, Amun, and
his wife were making love, Selket and Neith kept
guard so that they would not be disturbed. Ishtar, the
Mesopotamian Mother Goddess, was represented by
scorpions in her alter-ego as Lady of the Underworld.
Seven scorpions assisted Isis in the fight against her
enemies. The hero, Gilgamesh, encountered scorpion
men at sunset's gate during his epic experiences. In
ancient times, scorpion symbols and carvings were
worn as protective amulets, and Selket was one of
the four goddesses who stood guardian over Osiris's
body. It is also interesting that Selket was associated
with the glaring heat of the Sun for, as we now
know, scorpions have an extraordinary resistance to
intensive heat – even that of radiation. Isara, whose
symbol was the scorpion, was 'Queen of the Judgment Seat' to the ancient Mesopotamians, while
Sadrapa was the God of Healing of the ancient
Syrians, his emblems being the snake and the scorpion. He is also known as Satrapas, and under this
name was revered in parts of Greece. It is possible
to see in these ancient tales the beginnings of the

association of this zodiacal sign with death, the underworld and sexuality.

As we have seen in other cases, all that is good concerning the ancient deities was censored by Christian theology, leaving us with only the negative aspects. In this case, the excessive sexuality, the malicious, murderous sting. It is time that Scorpions stopped feeling apologetic about their supposed failings and recognised that they have a tender, nourishing side which, if developed, can bestow endless benefits on those in need. They should concentrate on the great energy given to them by their co-rulers, Mars and Pluto, and see that it is directed towards the care, sustenance and healing of humankind. Birth, death and regeneration are the aspects of life associated with this sign.

The world is undergoing a long transit of Pluto in Scorpio, and for the moment we see uppermost the destructive qualities of this. Everyone's mind is fixed on AIDS, death in all its inevitability, child abuse, violent crimes, Chernobyl and other atomic disasters (Pluto rules atomic radiation); even the tragedy of the cancer tests that went wrong in a Liverpool hospital. Scorpio-ruled cities such as Liverpool have been suffering the transit particularly badly, while Scorpio-ruled Russia has been having its lot improved, with *glasnost* and long-overdue reforms. Poland (Scorpio ascendant) is suffering from a more painful transformation. Both still have a very long way to go, however. Taurus countries have been getting the brunt of the Pluto opposition, and these include Ireland and Israel.

At present, our thoughts are focused on death and sex and violence. No one can deny that. These are all the negative aspect of Scorpio and Pluto, the great transformer. Remember that word: transform. It cannot happen without great upheaval, without things being altered, sometimes totally. People do not take easily to change. They fear it; they like the tried and true. They want life to be comfortable and easy – and who can blame them? But we are here to learn, and some lessons are tough, particularly for Scorpions, who are getting the brunt of this transit now and will continue to do so in the years to come. Lester Piggott and Ken Dodd are both Scorpio ruled.

I entirely agree with Liz Greene (see reading list), who has compared the transit of Pluto with the entry of the Goddess Inanna into the Underworld in her quest to save her beloved Tammuz. As the goddess went further and further into the depths, she had to remove a layer of clothing at each of the seven gates. This was her spiritual sacrifice, and also a casting off of worldly concerns. It was her willingness to show that she was prepared to lose everything in the name of love. This too was the origin of the famous dance of the seven veils, for it was not created to tempt men sexually. Inanna was successful in her quest, but she must have felt nervous and unsure as she stripped off her outer coverings, the symbols of her wealth and her connection with all that was dearest to her. In the end, she was reunited with Tammuz and the world blossomed again and was newly built. In the deepest trough of the Pluto transit, we too can feel as if we have lost all that we love most, all that keeps us happy and content, even the very foundations of our life. But they will be built anew and they will be better. There will be rewards and pleasant surprises at the end. We may find that we are very different at the end of this transit . . . and all for the better.

In the midst of all this gloom, people are coming to understand what Inanna instinctively knew: that love is all that matters. They are finding spiritual qualities in themselves that they did not know were there. They are nursing the fatally sick and accompanying them to the very gates of the Underworld. Nothing is forced upon us; we want these experiences. We need them. They are honing our spirits. There will be cures found – the natural way of healing and building up the immune system is already having excellent effects where established medicine has failed. Unfortunately, it is in the drug companies' interest to paint as black a picture of this new disease as possible, so that they can get larger grants for their work and make more millions when their 'wonder' drugs are discovered. They will argue that they are in the business because they care about people, but millions of animals will have died in painful research programmes, and two wrongs can never make a right.

Remember that Sadrapa was God of Healing. Remember that Selket was guardian of Isis's precious son, Horus, and that the scorpion is a devoted mother. It carries its young on its back for their first two weeks of life. The sting of the scorpion was used by Selket to protect the infant Horus, and to defend Isis against her foes. The sting was always to protect those in need; it was never used indiscriminately, and certainly not for evil purposes.

The self-defence of the scorpion can be savage and fatal to its enemies. At their worst, the human Scorpion stings vengefully and indiscriminately. All this is an appalling misdirection of their great powers. Revenge is always a terrible waste of energies that could be turned to the good of humankind.

Karmically, there is no cause without an effect, and all bad or evil thoughts or actions that we direct against others will return to us.

There is another symbol for the sign, and that is the eagle flying high above all that is crude, primitive and bestial. Positive Scorpions rise above the negative aspects of their sign. They are noble, loyal, supportive, protective, and will work with indomitable energies for the good of humankind. Gandhi had Scorpio rising. Indira Gandhi was Scorpio. Margaret Thatcher has Scorpio rising. St Augustine started life as a negative Scorpio and completed it as a most positive one. The intense stubbornness of the sign can be seen at its worst in Charles I and Marie Antoinette, both of whom were blind and deaf to all points of view but their own.

Now that Pluto is transiting this sign until late 1995, Scorpios have the most marvellous opportunity for self-transformation. They can rise above the twistings and turnings of mere mortals and discover enormous powers for good within themselves. Some will perhaps decide to self-destruct, to return at another time when things are easier for them. That is their prerogative. Others will battle on and find the pot of gold at the end of the rainbow, and they will put that 'gold' to good use on behalf of others.

Physically, this sign is small-boned and slight, never tall. Scorpios come in petite, dynamic packages! They have either dark, nearly black eyes with a piercing gaze that can be almost X-ray-like in intensity, or the very palest of blue eyes (for example, those of Linda Evans). Hair is dark to black, when the eyes are dark brown, and sometimes the two front teeth cross over one another a little, or there can be an almost cat-like expression of smouldering, exotic beauty, as in the case of Vivien Leigh and Hedy Lamarr. The upper lip thins when smiling, and this is one of the major pointers to Scorpio (the Duchess of York is Scorpio rising). When Mars is prominent, the hair can be flaming red. (The Duchess has Mars conjunct her sun sign.) When the eyes are very pale blue or grey, the hair is blonde or fair, and this is most often seen when Scorpio is on the ascendant. The 'petite, dynamic packages' include Lulu, Petula Clark and Jodie Foster – who was involved at a very early age in a Scorpio-style acting part in *Taxi Driver*. Margaret Mitchell, author of *Gone with the Wind*, was a Scorpio (and had the typical looks of the sign), and Scarlett O'Hara is a very Scorpio heroine, wilful and determined. She was of course played by Vivien Leigh – a Scorpio.

Scorpio voices are husky, gravelly or gritty, as with Demi Moore, Bob Hoskins, Charles Bronson, Richard Boon, Dickie Henderson and Fenella Fielding. Sometimes they can be harsh as corncrakes! The biting comment is another pointer to Scorpio, but this is more likely to be seen when this sign is deeply unhappy, or when the positive potential of Scorpio has not been realised. The Scorpio wit, when it does appear – and frequently this is a very serious sign without an obvious sense of humour, especially with Scorpio rising – is dry, cynical and sometimes biting, as with Peter Cook and Griff Rhys Jones.

The author of *Dracula*, Bram Stoker, was a Scorpio, and his world-famous book is obsessed with the Scorpio/Pluto concerns of death, rebirth and regeneration. Many of its scenes take place in bedrooms and graveyards. *Dracula* was written just before the discovery of the planet Pluto and is a prime example of how the imminent discovery of a planet can fill our minds with the particular qualities associated with it. Pluto is also about the disintegration of all that is dear and familiar to us, and the first to suffer from this were the Jews, Romanies and others who were torn from their families and sent to their deaths in the Second World War: the most tragic disintegration of family life that anyone could ever imagine. We are still suffering from the transformative effects of Pluto on family life generally. People have never before needed to make such an effort to protect and keep their families together; but there is nothing that could be more worth fighting for, surely.

The Scorpio child

Parents may never truly know what a Scorpio child is thinking, but may sometimes glimpse the seething turbulence beneath the debonair facade. Those dark, piercing eyes see and sense everything. They can see behind pretences; they can sense what people are thinking and feeling. That can be unnerving in a child, and if psychic gifts are also displayed early, then parents may feel at a loss as to how to deal with the situation. But it is perfectly normal for Scorpios to be psychic, perceptive and even mind-reading, and there is no cause for alarm. These Pluto-ruled children should never be treated as if they are extra-ordinary, for all children, whatever their gifts, need to feel perfectly normal. It is part of Scorpio's nature to be secretive and self-protective: look at Russia; look at Washington, USA! Like the crab of Cancer, the scorpion has a shell and will conceal itself behind it. The Scorpio child may sense that he or she is different in some way, and it is then up to the parents to reassure and apply some of the good old-fashioned comforts of mothering.

The keen, sharp, incisive Scorpio mind will show itself early. Nothing parents do will be forgotten. Scorpio memories go back a long way. They will, however, have a loyal friend in their Scorpio child, who will support them through thick and thin – if he knows that they are on his side. He (or she) will come out fighting furiously in their defence when need arises, and will also be possessive of his loved ones. The loyalty and protectiveness of Selket should be encouraged, and thoughts of vengeance discouraged. If they are told about the Scorpio eagle that flies high and is above such things, Scorpio children will be fascinated by such stories and eagerly ask for more. Those dark, piercing eyes will shine as they listen. They will be interested in many subjects, with an early fascination for the opposite sex. That too needs gentle guidance so that they don't plunge into the maelstrom before they can handle it. When mature, they are not as vulnerable as Virgo or as naive as Pisces – and parents might find themselves defending others against their Scorpio children as they get into their teens. Or, if the children are true to form, parents will never discover anything at all about their private lives.

Like Gemini, they need to have a regular routine of relaxation as part of their upbringing. The Mars/Pluto energies can become a coiled spring that will drive them to exhaustion and explosions of temperament. They may have tantrums. They may throw things and refuse to do what is wanted. It is very difficult to make Scorpios do something when they are determined to resist. They can be implacable. That is why it is essential for parents to build up good communications with them at an early age; without prying, for they will retreat and become more secretive. Opening their mail or reading their diaries will destroy their trust forever. They should know that parents are always there if needed. They must learn that honesty is the best policy, even if they have the wits to outdo everyone else; and that they can be of enormous help to those in need, the sick, the helpless – and that includes animals, too, for they will adore them. It is all too easy for that secretiveness and suspiciousness to turn inwards and for Scorpio to be so busy defending itself that it thinks of no one else.

A high-fibre diet is very important for the lower

regions that are ruled by this sign. One large salad a day is essential, so the child should be accustomed to crudités, raw greens, fresh fruit and seeds. Wheatgerm, wholemeal bread, sunflower seeds, pollen and Vitamin C contain the goodness that the reproductive organs need. Crisps, chips, chocolate biscuits, pork pies and Coca-Cola do not! They are Foods from the Dead Zone (see appendix), and have a detrimental effect on the body. Scorpio children will probably eat fast and have smallish appetites, so it is important that what they eat is nutritious – and that they are taught to chew each mouthful carefully. Meals should never be eaten when tense, and there should be time to relax after eating.

Health

The coiled-spring energies need to be regularly recharged with relaxation and tranquillity. Think of the curving tail of the scorpion that will bend right over to sting its opponent – or itself. Without proper attention to health and mental relaxation, that sting can bite deep. When they feel fit and vigorous (as they usually do) Scorpios will laugh off the need for a little yoga or stretching exercises, but if they are suddenly hit with weariness or that below par feeling and they haven't any method of coping with it, then they can feel very alone and frightened. More than anything else, they dread feeling helpless. They may look on simple health care as admitting to frailty when it is nothing of the sort. Believing themselves to be invincible is foolish, and leaves them unprepared and vulnerable. They pride themselves on being logical and shrewd – but is it either of these to believe that you can drive yourself at breakneck pace indefinitely, without pause, and never suffer as a result?

All that may be needed is a few minutes of simple yoga breathing each morning, taking a deep, slow breath while counting to five, then breathing out slowly while again counting to five. After a few of these breaths, strength and calm will flood the body. Deep breathing is valuable whenever they feel their innards tightening into a knot. They may, in fact, have forgotten what life is like without that knot of tension. Tension permeates the whole of the body and the mind. It is like poison ivy: it creeps and clings and tightens its tendrils round muscles and vital organs and then lets its poison spill through them. That famous acid tongue of the Scorpio will not be soothed by an acid body. The diet should be highly alkaline, with fruits and vegetables making up a large portion of it. Meat, milk, cheese, white bread, tea, coffee and alcohol are all acid-forming. Scorpios may be in the habit of lunging from one cup of coffee to another and rushing their meals, or fill up with junky snacks. Like Aries, they may be absolutely positive that they are immortal and that such bad habits could never harm them. The shell of the scorpion can make them very smug. However, they depend upon their famous intuition, and such a diet will eventually make them feel clogged and shackled, physically and mentally.

If they are already feeling sour and bitter and spend much of their time glowering, then they need to revitalise their diet completely, throwing out all acid-forming and junk foods, trashy drinks, white sugar and chocolate (it is dark and dangerous). A one-day fruit fast would establish the foundations of a new person – two days would be even better, if there is the chance to spend some quiet time alone and rest and relax. Eat only one type of fruit at each meal and drink mineral waters and mint or pepper-mint herbal teas, keep warm and, if feeling tired, lie down and rest. An Epsom-salt bath will help them to expel body toxins. First, add a pound of Epsom salts to a comfortably warm bath and relax in it for twenty minutes, then splash down with cold water, wrap in a towel and go to bed for at least twenty minutes to sweat out the poisons.

Each day, the skin should be brushed, always upwards towards the heart, using a bristle brush or rough mitt and a circular motion. The skin is the biggest organ of elimination, and this will keep the liver toned up.

If it is a case of feeling jaded from years of the wrong food eaten too quickly, Scorpios can try the Hay diet. The basic rules of this are as follows: never eat grains with protein. Apple and cheese is allowed, but not bread and cheese. Never mix potatoes with protein, or eat two kinds of protein together. There is a complete list in *Food Combining For Health* (see appendix). Sir John Mills (a Pisces) is a keen follower of the Hay diet and has been for many years. He attended three parties for his eightieth birthday and looks extremely fit. The idea behind this diet is that eating certain foods together taxes the digestive processes and causes obesity and liverishness plus other ailments. Many people have lost weight on this diet, or have found their lost energies restored. It can also help sluggish systems, indigestion and heart-burn. After keeping foods separated in the way that is advocated for some weeks, try eating a normal meal with meat and potatoes mixed and then a pudding. You will feel remarkably bloated afterwards.

Intestinal flora have been much in the news lately with the anti-candida diet, and as Scorpio rules the 'underworld' of the body, those born under this sign should keep it in mind. Sugar (even fruit sugar, fructose), fermented foods, yeast-containing foods, alcohol, mushrooms, blue cheeses and ageing nuts can exacerbate the problem, but first there must be a reason for the healthy intestinal flora to be destroyed and the unhealthy ones to grow. Antibiotics, vaccines, the pill and cortisone are all incriminated as destroyers. Unfortunately, children have been lavishly prescribed antiobiotics for over twenty years now – some have even been given them for simple colds and viruses against which they have no power. It is essential that live plain yoghurt is eaten daily during a course of antibiotics. A course of acidophilus will be beneficial, too (see appendix, 'The Yeast Beast'). Commercial, sweetened yoghourts are useless – and so are pasteurised ones. Vitamin C is important, too, and after a course of any of these drugs, the immune system must be built up again. Think of the immune system as a fortress. Without it, you are defenceless. When you are vaccinated, or take the pill, antibiotics or cortisone, your fortress is under attack. I am not saying that these treatments are not of value, especially in times of epidemic. They can be life-savers. However, everyone who takes one of these courses must take steps to protect their immune system.

Without the protective intestinal flora, candida can imprison the body. If you have seen yeast bubbling and growing when sugar is added to it, then you will know how candida flourishes in the defenceless body. Women who have taken the birth control pill may well have suffered thrush because the pill affects the body's absorption of vitamins. Live plain yoghourt is the answer, plus the anti-candida diet as formulated by Leon Chaitow. Acidophilus powder or pills are essential, too. As Leon Chaitow says, sufferers may need to keep on this diet for some time, because once candida has a grip, it can be difficult to move it. Far better not to let it get a grip.

There are many symptoms of candida apart from the appearance of thrush patches in the mouth. Feelings of drained tiredness, of irritability, bloating or depression may be present. Ignoring candida leaves your body with its fortress defences down, and you are then extremely vulnerable.

A word to male Scorpios: you may feel invincibly fit and carry heavy weights without trouble, but it would be as well to lift weights with knees bent and arms close to the body, because hernia can be a Scorpio problem.

And as Scorpio rules the reproductive and sexual system, there must be a word about infections in this area. Vitamins C and A are great protectors against infection, as is a healthy, mainly raw-food diet with all its living enzymes. A strong immune system is vital. Some people get infections; others do not. It largely depends on the state of the immune system. However, even if the most perfect diet is being eaten and there is every sign of health and fitness, impulsive exposure to possible sources of infection is foolish. Scorpios must not forget that this is their weakest area and they must take steps to protect it. There are a lot of nasty bugs about these days and they have caught hold because immune systems have been weakened by drugs, the pill, vaccination, antibiotics – and junk-food addictions.

Herbal teas for Scorpio

Ruby Red by Floradix. Red Zinger. Passion flower for premenstrual tension and menopause. See Taurus for herbs for the throat. For males who suffer from an excess of Scorpio sexual desire: hops have a calming effect on the sexual organs. In ancient times, lettuce juice was recommended for an excess of lust. Chamomile and valerian for restlessness.

9

SAGITTARIUS

Niels Bohr, Nobel prizewinning Danish physicist, was asked why he had hung a horseshoe above his door. He replied, 'It's odd about horseshoes; even if you don't believe in them they work.'

Sagittarius the Archer: c. 22 November–c. 22 December   Element: Fire. Planetary rulership: Jupiter. Physical rulership: hips and thighs; liver; base of the spine. By polarity with Gemini: the lungs.

Destiny of Sagittarius: not to kick out at others when things don't go the way they hoped. To brighten the world by making people laugh.

Herbs for Sagittarius: dandelion (to help the work of liver and kidneys); sage; chervil; carrots.

Vital vitamins and minerals for Sagittarius: B complex to protect the liver against the effects of alcohol; vitamin E (Canadian racehorses were given vitamin E, as a result of which their number of wins rose by 66 per cent within a year. The vitamin E also calmed their skittish temperaments and improved their appetites). Inositol (a B vitamin) for sleeplessness. Calcium and vitamin D taken together for strong bones. For cirrhosis of the liver: B complex, vitamins A, D, E and K to replace stores lost due to the disease.

Gems for Sagittarius: jacinth or hyacinth (a reddish-blue stone); topaz. Topaz comes in yellow, brownish yellow, white, blue and red. It was believed that topazes guarded against the evil eye, witchcraft and untrustworthy friends. They were used to improve the health and vigour of the liver, guard against madness and insomnia and to enliven the taste buds.

The myth behind the motivation

Sagittarians can be sporty or pious, philosophical or bawdy and Rabelaisian, the life and soul of the party or gifted musicians and singers. Contrary to popular belief, not all centaurs were half horse. Some were half ox and some half ass – which could account for the great diversity of the sign! The original centaurs were unruly beasts, not accountable to anyone, mule-headed (it's hard to stay mentally aloof from your equine half!), pugnacious and riotous. The children of Centaurus, son of Apollo, the centaurs were invited to the wedding feast of Hippodamia, where they imbibed too much wine and behaved very badly indeed, forcing their advances on some of the female guests. Hercules and Theseus were at the feast and became so enraged that they and their companions went to the aid of the women, fought off the centaurs and sent them into exile. Later, there was a childish dispute over Hercules's use of the centaurs' wine, in which the wisest centaur, Chiron, was accidentally wounded by a poisoned arrow. So intense was his suffering that he surrendered his immortality in exchange for the relief of death. Jupiter responded by placing Chiron in the heavens, where he became known as Sagittarius.

Chiron was no ordinary centaur. He embodied all that was greatest and wisest in humankind, after learning his youthful wild lessons well. Having fought the young Olympians, he was transformed into half man, half horse by Apollo, from which time he did only good deeds – educating Achilles, Hercules, Aesculapius, Jason and others. Each of them spent time alone with Chiron in the wilderness, emerging wiser and better for it. Chiron also taught the human race how to employ healing herbs and plants.

It is quite possible for the entire range of centaurian behaviour to be seen in one Sagittarian. They can be impetuous, charging headlong into matters without thinking out their actions; they can be headstrong, rebellious, difficult and argumentative, pugnacious and even punch-drunk. They can also be great visionaries, with an immense store of spiritual wisdom, and a fiery strength and courage that can make them indomitable. Their trusting nature can all too often become a surprising naïveté, however. They have an Amazonian approach to life, demanding freedom and lack of restraint for themselves. They will do what they will. When others complain, they are taken aback. How could people be so difficult, so lacking in understanding? No one is going to tell wild horses what to do!

The wilderness beckons, where Chiron was at his most fulfilled, and there is no Sagittarian alive who has not hungered at one time or another for challenge and adventure, the unworn trail. George Eliot was born under this sign. She was one of the most liberated Victorian women and dictated her own lifestyle. Grace Darling displayed all the courage and fearlessness of the sign. Toulouse-Lautrec was another Sagittarian who did it his way – as do Frank Sinatra and Lord Longford. Mary Stuart, beautiful, wilful Queen of Scots, did it her way, too, and paid the ultimate penalty. Sagittarian John Bunyan wrote of the difficult way of the pilgrim in *Pilgrim's Progress*, a very Chiron-like book, and Saki wrote of the beast in men.

In the representation of Sagittarius, the noble horse

with the torso of a man, the bow and arrow is being aimed at far distant horizons; but remember the weapon that destroyed Chiron. Sagittarians can be their own worst enemies, wounding themselves with their own arrows, for what is not aimed for the good of others can turn in upon itself. General Custer, Sagittarius at its most negative, died in a rain of arrows, taking many others to their deaths along with him. At another time, such unflinching courage and unshakable belief as that displayed by the Sagittarian Winston Churchill saved our country from the horrors of invasion. Bravery, fortitude and strength without the right, selfless motivation, however, can become nothing more than an erratic, wilful ego.

There is the wonderfully strange, beckoning wilderness, and there is the wilderness where people are despatched when they have offended against society. One is the wilderness of Chiron and one the exile of the drunken centaurs who turned Hippodamia's wedding feast into a battlefield. All too easily that freedom-loving Sagittarian impetuosity can become a hell-bent craving to indulge the whim of the moment regardless of the needs of others. With a showbusiness outlet, this rebellious drive can sometimes become acceptable, even when displayed in a foul-mouthed or outrageous way, as with Bette Midler, Richard Pryor, Billy Connolly and Pamela Stephenson, who undoubtedly get a kick out of shocking their audiences – or trying to. Of course, sometimes there is a kickback, but they just have to live with that. The borderline between the wilderness of Chiron, where Sagittarians yearn to be, and the wilderness of the exiled centaurian wedding guests is sometimes an extremely fine one. One foolish, impetuous move, and the damage can be done.

Sagittarius is a Fire sign and, as with Leo and Aries, there can be a danger of burn-up. Passion, haste and headlong impulsiveness can propel Sagittarians only for so long before they come to grief. It is important that they cultivate the Chiron side of their natures, the wisdom and vision, the healing qualities.

The connection with the hip and thigh can be traced back many centuries. This part of an animal was dedicated to the gods when sacrificed. In *Revelations* 19:16, there is mention of the name King of Kings being written upon the thigh, a place associated with sagacity at that time. In *Genesis*, we have the account of Jacob wrestling at Peniel, and the reason why the children of Israel 'eat not the sinew of the hip which is upon the hollow of the thigh'. (A horse can kick out at those standing near it and wound them or it can carry them nobly on its back in the cause of good.)

Ruled by expansive, lucky Jupiter, Sagittarius is one of the money-making signs. Sagittarians can sometimes make money almost without thinking about it; they can prosper early and become embarrassingly rich . . . except that they are unfamiliar with embarrassment. In that headlong rush to secure a comfortable stall for themselves in the world that exiled their centaurian ancestors, they may never think of those in need, and in the end find themselves lonely and alone. However, it is far more likely that they will give generously to the poor and unfortunate. They may forget the friends who have helped them along the way, though. A galloping horse gathers no moss!

They can be strange and perplexing to those who do not study astrology. Outsiders, rebels, people who think, talk and behave differently, they can be difficult to understand. Australia is not ruled by this sign for nothing! In some ways they are not unlike Aquarians, who also must have their personal freedom, but the centaurian has an altogether more fiery and blunt approach. The bow and arrow held by the Archer can point to their visionary minds, the far-sighted eye on distant horizons; or, at worst, it can be the poisoned arrow that caused Chrion so much agony he surrendered his immortality to be free of its pain. Sagittarians can make the choice for themselves. They can be great visionaries, of immense help and support to humankind; or they can injure themselves – and others – with their poisoned arrows. Sometimes they transform the poison into what amounts almost to tragic humour, turning life's worst calamities and neuroses into wit, as with James Thurber and Woody Allen. Or their books will have an inspirational or mythological theme, as with C. S. Lewis; a reworking of mythology or culture, as with Poul Anderson; or a concentration on the matter of alienation, as with Frederik Pohl. Sagittarian authors often like to create characters who have a difficult time in foreign or alien lands, as in *Gulliver's Travels* by Jonathan Swift (who was also well known for the blunt Sagittarian comment). Mark Twain, John Milton and William Blake (who stood trial for high treason after speaking too bluntly about the King) were also born under this sign.

Physically, Sagittarians are strongly built, and the men easily gain muscle. Eyes are medium brown, as is hair, and many Sagittarian men have quite a mane of hair, along with a beard. The legs can be an outstanding feature, either well-shaped and strong (Tina Turner, Betty Grable; Raquel Welch and Kate Bush have this sign rising) or bowed. The hips and thighs can be very powerful, or suffer from a lack of nutrients while growing. Sagittarian men especially have an appearance of barely harnessed energy, as if they long to gallop headlong into all and everything. Television presenter Mike Scott, who is totally sceptical about astrology, is a good example. They may be very restless and talkative, and have a wonderful gift for putting their foot in it verbally and upsetting people, like Jonathan King. The blunt remark is one pointer to spotting this sign. A good singing voice (by polarity with Gemini) is another pointer, and there are many famous singing Sagittarians. They can have a hearty sense of humour, even a braying laugh (Derek Jameson), and the shape of the face may be long and narrow (Alicia Markova; Julie Harris; Boris Karloff). Or there may be a long, flattish nose, not unlike a horse's with the eyes set high, like playwright John Osborne. Hips are narrow, shoulders and teeth strong.

The Sagittarian child

Impatient, impulsive, galloping into tight corners, losing their tempers easily, gawky, all legs and arms, but physically tough and broadening out early, Sagittarian children fill the house with noise and activity. If doors are closed, they want entry urgently and may almost resemble skittish stallions backing up against the framework and kicking out with their hoofs. They throw their heads back and laugh with a braying or whinnying sound. They toss their heads and fidget with their feet and love to be the centre of attention. On a stage, like Leo, they will love every minute. Music will soothe and stir them and they may be exceptionally gifted musically, either at singing (Maria Callas) or with an instrument. They may be hot-headed rebels as they get into their mid-teens, and all that will hold them to their parents then is an earlier friendly and well-established relationship, because they will not take anyone's advice at this stage. They are emphatically positive

that they know what they want to do and that they
are right, right, right. Later, that rebellious fire may
well be put to invaluable use, for time transforms it
into a great courage. Edith Cavell was born under
this sign.

Film world Sagittarians include Walt Disney and
Steven Spielberg, and film director Busby Berkeley,
who gave us years of beautiful, dancing legs to
watch. Once those tumultuous energies are directed
properly, there can be a richness of achievement on
an astonishing scale.

There will be warmth and fun and lots of frolics
with Sagittarian children and providing that parents
keep them on a loose rein, they will always love
them. (That applies to everyone in a Sagittarian's life,
not just parents.) Bouncy and buoyant, argumentative, cheeky, ebullient, well meaning, blundering,
outspoken (how *do* you teach them tact?), they
frequently embarrass their parents. Fortunately, they
can use up a lot of their energy in sport, where they
will excel. Those strong Sagittarian hips and thighs
may also lead them into the ballet, or dance (Fred
Astaire had this sign rising), or horse-riding.
However, they must have a vocation, as they cannot
take the strictures of this sort of discipline unless
they are fired with enthusiasm. They can't tolerate
restrictions and do not take kindly to conventions.
(Ian Botham is a Sagittarian, and so is Eddy the
Eagle.) Parents may spend a lot of time explaining
why certain things have to be done – and those
reasons had better be good ones!

They should have a calcium-rich diet as they grow,
to protect those hips and thighs, which can all too
easily become bowed. (Astrological rulership of a
bodily area means that it can be extra strong, or extra
vulnerable.) As they are sporadic eaters, it is not
always easy to see that they get all the nutrients they

need. Sometimes they may rush at food; at other times, they're not interested. A daily multivitamin will help to level things out. If they are involved in strenuous sport or exercise, parents should give them a multimineral rich diet, too, or consult a nutritionally trained naturopath about a diet chosen especially for their needs.

Like Gemini, their polar opposites, they can become so tightly wound up that they can't relax and then they will thrash about in bed and complain loudly. Music may be the answer here – with earphones. Their interests will be eclectic from an early age, and they will enjoy books of knowledge and colourful fiction packed with adventure and discovery. As they reach the lawful age for driving, they must receive proper instruction and be fully aware that their parents care deeply for them, because they can be reckless on the roads. A car is like an arrow, and they want to go places fast.

They will have a close intuitive relationship with horses and will love riding. John Francome, who writes racing thrillers, is a Sagittarian . . . and although epic-length novel-writing is too restricting for the average members of this sign, who often find it impossible to sit still, they may enjoy writing about their favourite activities. Travel journalism or exploration would suit them, and there are still some mysterious places left in the world. They don't do things by halves, and if they have an interest, they will throw themselves into it wholeheartedly – so they need a little sensible guidance beforehand. They may be so accomplished at so many things that they become restless and bored. Childhood can be very restrictive for children who like to do things on a big scale, without people breathing down their necks, but it is a time to ensure that they don't get into mischief.

In later years, those jolly, jovial Sagittarians can be rather liverish, out of sorts and tetchy if they have been in the habit of rushing their food and overindulging in rich dishes. If they have grown up being aware of the dangers of too much cream and fat and dairy foods, and the benefits of fresh fruit and the occasional all-fruit day to cleanse the system, then they may well avoid the worst symptoms. Growing children should not be stinted on healthy calories, of course – especially if they are regularly involved in sports or other demanding activities at school. Nor should small children be given extra bran. But it is far wiser for a teenager to know what positive steps they can take if they are worried about an excess of pounds. Then they will not get involved with dangerous diets. Wholefoods are rich in zinc. Refined foods have lost their zinc. Without this mineral, the appetite can be drastically affected. Shortage of zinc is implicated in anorexia. No one need be given a medal for realising that if a child is playing hard and working hard, he or she needs extra calories, extra vitamins and minerals: calcium and vitamin D for strong hips and thighs, fish oils and vitamin E and octasonal (extracted from vitamin E) for stamina. Wholegrains, proteins, fruit, eggs, lamb's liver, wheatgerm, sesame seeds, oranges (for calcium), soya, and goat's or cow's milk should all play a regular part in Sagittarian children's diets. Snacks of fatty crisps, hot dogs, chocolate and biscuits will give them bouts of low blood sugar that will make them grumpy and tired.

It is as well to mention the old and very bad habit of filling up with sugary foods before a sporting event. There is a price to be paid for this, for while the pancreas is struggling to deal with an excess of refined sugar, the body is also being stressed to the limits by physical activity. This can lead to arthritis in later years, and low-blood sugar problems. The best meal before an event is fruit – pieces of orange and grapefruit or pineapple – a light, easily digested food that is full of fructose and fruit fibre. Fruits have fibre so that the fructose can be digested harmlessly. It is only when the fibre is stripped off (as with sugar cane) and we eat the refined residue that we are taking that drastic step away from Nature and endangering our systems.

Health

Being the life and soul of the party can take its toll, and after the guests have gone home Sagittarians may collapse. Unhappy Sagittarians may drink to excess and precipitate liver trouble, but as this sign is ruled by Jupiter the Luck Bringer, they are capable of falling on their feet where others would be lying in the gutter. Money may drop their way without any effort, so they may become lazy and out of condition. It is no easy task to get a Sagittarian back into the realms of the fit and vigorous when they have let themselves go. It is rather like trying to make a cart horse into a Nijinsky. A sluggish liver affects the entire system, but an all-fruit day once a week and six glasses of mineral water daily will put them on the winning track. Dandelion coffee is a good liver and kidney cleanser.

Centaurian or not, they may be prone to riding accidents, where the hip and thigh area will be extra vulnerable. It may not be a bad idea for them to practise falling, so that they are well prepared. Bones can be kept strong with calcium and vitamin D and weight-bearing exercise. White sugar leaches the calcium from the bones, so should be avoided.

Tinned fish such as mackerel, sardines and salmon are an excellent source of this mineral.

Herbal teas for Sagittarius

Any new and unusual herb tea. Peppermint and mint to aid the liver in digestion. Morning Starter by Jill Davies. Dandelion coffee, to tone liver and kidneys. Freshly made lemon tea for liver disorders.

10

CAPRICORN

At the moment of birth, a child's etheric
body . . . soft and malleable as wax,
receives the imprint of stellar influences.
. . . When a child first draws breath,
the heavens put their seal on its etheric
body and fix the horoscope in which
the child's destiny is written.
Omraam Mikhael Aivanhov

Capricorn the Sea Goat: c. 23 December–c. 19
January   Planetary ruler: Saturn. Element: Earth.
Physical rulership: skeleton, knees, teeth, skin. By
polar opposition to Cancer: the digestion.

Destiny of Capricorn: to learn to put people before
material matters; to give spiritual and emotional
support to those in need.

Herbs for Capricorn: elm, for skin problems and rheumatism. Celery (stalks and seeds) for rheumatic
complaints. Sage and meadowsweet are dissemi-
nators of uric acid. Chamomile is soothing and anti-
inflammatory. Burdock and fumitory are two of the
blood-cleansing herbs for clear skin.

Vital vitamins and minerals for Capricorn: calcium and
vitamin D for strong bones and teeth. Vitamin A and
B complex for the skin – and also oil of evening
primrose. Vitamin C for connective tissue, especially
of the spine, and for healthy gums.

Gems for Capricorn: jet. Smoky quartz. Black onyx.
Orange carnelian (also recommended for Taureans,

for the voice) for Capricorns' low spirits and rheumatic complaints. Jet has been used for ornamentation since the Bronze Age. Whitby jet from Yorkshire was prized in Victorian times, when jet was worn as mourning jewellery. It was burnt in magic rituals, its smoke being evil-smelling, and this process was also employed to heal the sick. French jet, an imitation, is glass based and much more fragile. Onyx is associated with Philip the Apostle and is also used as mourning jewellery. It is said to aid hearing and to help its wearer settle karmic debts during the first half of life – the years that Capricorns find most stressful.

The myth behind the motivation

Very few people born under Capricorn understand the true duality of their natures. The Sea-Goat, born from the primeval waters of Mother Earth, is half land creature, half sea creature. It is because the lower half is fish that it is inclined to be forgotten, for the sea washes over it, concealing all its deepest mysteries, while there is undue concentration on the worldly strivings of the upper half.

Chronos (Saturn), God of Time, is more than a little infamous for his devouring ways. His brother, Titan, gave him the world as his kingdom, and he promised in return that he would sire no sons. When sons were born, he swallowed them. Only Jupiter (Zeus) escaped his father's wrath, for his mother Rhea hid him away in a cave on Mount Ida, where he was suckled by Amaltheia, the daughter of Melissus, King of Crete. Amaltheia was a she-goat who flowed with nectar and ambrosia, which she gave willingly to the young god. He rewarded her for her devotion by placing her in the heavens as Capella. This story reveals the two types of Capricorn: the Saturnian, who will pursue material ambitions to the exclusion of all else (the workaholic is the modern example of this) and the Amaltheian, who cares deeply for the suffering and the helpless and will spend his or her life in dedicated service. Her Majesty the Queen has Capricorn rising, and Albert Schweitzer is another example of the selfless higher Capricorn, as are Joan of Arc and Martin Luther King.

Unfortunately, because of the land-creature, sea-creature division of the sign, Capricorns find it difficult to acknowledge or understand the two sides of their nature. They may be ruthlessly ambitious, fighting against the clock to accrue money, like Scrooge, and never thinking of others – or divinely selfless and caring nothing for their own material benefits. This is the paradox of a sign that normally pursues moderation in all things.

Saturn was also the Roman God of Agriculture, for time, the harvest and the cycle of the seasons were of vital importance to the ancients. If the harvest failed, then so did they. During the Roman Saturnalia, held at the darkest part of the year (near our Christmas time) it was traditional for slaves to be waited upon by their masters and mistresses, and candles were exchanged as gifts, to symbolise the light that would brighten the darkness and ensure the return of the unconquered Sun (or son). This symbolic rebirth of Light was adopted to excellent advantage by the Christian Church in later years.

Capricorns can spread either darkness or light. Out of touch with the reality of their true natures as all too many are today, they may consider themselves somewhat dark . . . gloomy, morose, depressive, absorbed with material matters and scowling when these don't progress as they wish. Separated from their spiritual halves by the wash of the waves, they may feel that there is little left for them to do except strive after money and security. The acquisition of money will thrill them to the core; its loss will depress them utterly. Yet awareness is all that is needed, for what is hidden and unacknowledged can create many psychological problems.

It will not be easy for them to get in touch with that sea-covered half if they have been unaware of it until now, but if they persevere, they will be much happier. If they have had a tendency to drown their sorrows when the going gets tough (not that Capricorns often shirk their responsibilities), now they will know why. Deep down, there is a spiritual side to them that is crying out for release. They may sense it as choked emotions that they are unable or unwilling to release. It is no use trying to keep the hatch shut on these feelings: they will only be doing themselves and those they love a disservice. Capricorn-ruled India is one of the most spiritual countries in the world and the methods employed there to develop and strengthen the spiritual nature are ones that will benefit Western Capricorns, too: meditation, yoga, chanting, and Ayurvedic medicine for ailments. A feeling of unease or embarrassment when beginning meditation or yoga is to be expected, but perseverance is the key. A tape that plays the sound of the sea will be helpful and remind them of their submerged oceanic half. Handel's *Water Music* or *Fingal's Cave* can also stir those hidden depths.

If Capricorns have never thought of doing good deeds such as voluntary work, then they should think of it now. Caring for others is a major way to work out those glooms. Think of Amaltheia, who took the little infant Jupiter to her breast and fed him on nectar and ambrosia until he grew into the King of Gods. The rewards for unselfishness can be enormous – and I do not mean of the material variety. Brooders and scowlers hurt only themselves.

There was another goat in ancient myth – Pan, whose name means 'All'. He was God of Nature and the wild woods, a terrifying, consuming energy force from which we get the word panic, because everyone panicked when he was on the loose. He was a very rustic figure, sparkling-eyed, wicked and twinkling, playing his eerie Pan pipes that sent delicious fearful shivers down the spines of those who heard them. Even before the Greeks, the goat was considered to be a figure of fecundity. In Egypt, he was Ba-neb-Djedet, and worshipped at Mendes, where women sacrificed to him when they wanted children. (A later Christian age called him Satan and he is now pictured as the Tarot Devil.) There is little of this fecundity to be seen in the modern Capricorn. They have small families and are not renowned for going on the rampage. Work and serious application has divorced them from Mother Nature, and they need to find this old agrarian self in gardens and woodlands and wild places. Building a pond that will flourish with wild life is one good way . . . or encouraging frogs (sacred to the Great Goddess) and fish and considering their ways through the seasons . . . or walking in the woods at dusk and practising putting out feelers to sense the natural energies swirling around in the growing darkness.

Although serious-minded, Capricorns can be brilliantly witty, and many of the sign are zany comedians – it is their way of throwing off the Saturnine glooms that beset them. Kenny Everett, Rowan Atkinson (wonderful as the Saturnine, scheming Blackadder), Dyan Cannon and Tracey Ullman are all born under this sign. They light the world with their humour and show us the best side of Saturn. Any sign associated with Water will be unfathomable at times, and

Capricorn has Cancer as its polar opposite, so there is a double dose of Crab and Sea-Goat. Being Earth-ruled can be both a blessing and an impediment, for it can strengthen and support, or increase the alienation from the sea-covered half. Many Capricorns need time alone; they can be quiet people and yet their witty remarks can be hilarious and so unexpected if you do not know them well. It is beneficial for them to spend their time alone in gardens or wild woods, rekindling their natural selves. Concrete and glass stifle them and encourage their alienation from their watery halves.

Physically, they are small-boned and of medium height, with dark eyes that do not like meeting another's gaze. Their hair is dark brown to black, fine and straight, and lacks lustre. Their skin is on the sallow side and they tan easily. The Capricorn nose is a smaller, sharper version of the Roman nose. There may be small bumps between the brows, as if goats' horns would like to sprout there. Eye-colouring is hazel to greenish-hazel or dark. They have serious expressions and do not smile easily. Some never smile, not even in their publicity photos. Norman Tebbit is Capricorn rising and very Saturnine in appearance. Rosalie Crutchley, Sissy Spacek, Humphrey Bogart, Robert Duvall, Arthur Scargill, Richard Briers, David Bailey and Malcolm McLaren are just a few examples of Capricorns with an unsmiling public face. Ben Kingsley is totally Capricorn physically (and played superbly in *Gandhi*); Capricorn's rule gives Indians their small build and dark colouring. These subjects can sometimes be quite plain and dress so plainly that they blend into the background and remain unnoticed, but those with the Earth-sign bone structure can be extraordinarily beautiful (Marlene Dietrich; Cary Grant). Capricorn rising can sometimes give an extra plainness or even some physical deformity. This is one of the 'slim' signs; Capricorns do not have a weight problem.

Capricorn writers approach a subject deeply and reflectively. They may write about the problems and dilemmas of greed and acquisitiveness, the battle between good and evil, as in Tolkien's *Lord of the Rings* and Robert Silverberg's *The Book of Skulls*, a story of self-seeking greed for the power of immortality, and the final price that must be paid for such ambitions. Silverberg's *Tower of Glass* is a story of disillusionment and coming to terms with reality (a very Capricorn concern). *Dying Inside* tells of a man who has become corrupted materially by his own exploitation of his telepathic powers, only to find them diminishing. Loss of status, of power and position, are fears that chill Capricorn – and yet deep inside they know that for their spiritual development, they need some tough experiences.

The Capricorn child

Parents may worry over their quiet, withdrawn Capricorn child, thinking that he or she will never conquer the social graces and be able to converse in a natural, unselfconscious way. In this, they can help these children most by not trying to force them. Pressure will only make them withdraw even more. Reflective and composed, they will have a mature outlook in many ways but, like Virgoan children, they need to be given time to come out of their shells. Support and backing are the greatest things they can be given. They need no teaching that emotions are best controlled. They should be encouraged to weep if they feel the need, and told that tears are healing and should never be suppressed. (This applies to boys, too, of course. Girls do not have the problem to the same extent. The boys of this sign have enough to cope with without parents who chastise them for showing their emotions.)

Reading is high on their list of pleasures and they will be inordinately happy when buried in a book. (The Sea-Goat enjoys reading in the bath, too.) Living through literature is also a way of facing the emotional side of themselves without distress. They may adopt a certain character in a book, or from history, and hero-worship them avidly. This should not be discouraged unless it is interfering with their own development. Capricorns have Pisces in the third house (the house of the mind) and they can be deeply involved in fantasy of every variety. As they appear to be so practical and serious to others, no one may ever guess at the vivid fantasies in their inner minds. Of course, balance is essential in all things, but if they show any talent at writing it should be warmly encouraged. Writing fiction is an excellent and safe outlet for emotion, feelings and fantasy.

The Capricorn rulership of teeth and bones makes the child born under this sign very vulnerable to sugary foods, for sugar leaches calcium from the bones and the body then excretes it. Eventually, the bones become fragile. Our ancestors had far healthier teeth than ours. Their sweetening was raw honey collected by hand and no machines 'purified' it. It was a limited form of sweetening, too, and only the fortunate few had access to it. Today, from birth onwards, children are plied with refined sugar. It is one of the cruellest things to put white sugar in a baby's bottle, not only denying him (or her) Nature's blessing of mother's milk, but also feeding them a denatured, processed sugar that has no nourishment and which their body cannot handle. The old-fashioned fibrous diet is beneficial to the teeth and gums. They are made for chewing and crunching and munching, not for sloppy, sweet foods which are swallowed straight down. More teeth are lost through gum disease than decay, so even if a child's teeth are strong, he needs healthy gums to hold them securely. Once, gum disease was seen only in older people; now, even children have it – and soft, sugary foods are the cause. Sugar is like a germ: put it anywhere in the mouth or stomach and it will begin its insidious damage. It comes under many names, as I have said before: including glucose syrup, dextrose, sucrose, maltose and glucose. All these have exactly the same effect as white sugar. Refined white flour, soft and creamy in texture, clings to the teeth and gums and starts the plaque forming that will eventually damage the roots. Mother Nature gives us her sugar along with fibre: fruit; sugar cane; sugar beet; honeycomb. It is only when the sweetness is removed from the fibre that it causes the damage. People may think that cleaning the teeth after eating is enough to prevent the damage, but we have a bony skeleton as our bodily framework and once sugar is in the stomach it can reach any part of us it cares to harm. Unfortunately, the sugar industry spends multi-millions each year on jolly, colourful adverts to promote the eating of candy and confectionery. If a child is taught this, and raised on wholefoods and fruit, he or she is unlikely to have those crucifying dips in energy which make it so vulnerable to denatured food and drinks. It can be great fun for a child to grow sprouted seeds, and the process is simple. They are a complete protein, full of nourishment and energy, crunchy and nutty, and ideal for children. Alfalfa, beans, legumes . . . all can be experimented with, and the child will have the pleasure of watching the tiny shoots appearing from the seed and the self-satisfaction of growing his or her own food.

Canned drinks may contain seven teaspoons of white sugar. Even the diet drinks contain phosphorus, which reacts against calcium with similar results to sugar – and each diet drink destroys some vitamin C. Imagine how much more harmful that is to the smaller child's body. Just a few days on an old-fashioned diet of fresh, raw vegetables, fruit and healthy protein can begin the improvement in the condition of the gums.

It is better still to begin building a child's healthy teeth before he or she is born. Women should make sure that their diet is good before they get pregnant. What affects their teeth and bones will affect the baby's. The ideal is to get fit some months before trying to conceive, by taking multivitamins and minerals with a healthy diet, raw foods, fruit and first-class protein. Canned fish is full of calcium and protects the heart. Healthy babies can't be built out of white sugar, white flour, crisps and chips – although many people try. Smoking, of course, is out – and so is alcohol. People may have the freedom to damage themselves, but they do not have the freedom to damage their unborn child – and that applies to men, too. It has been clearly shown in research projects that men who smoke and drink can produce damaged or inferior sperm as a result.

Capricorn also rules the skin, and if a little Capricorn has skin rashes or irritations, oil of evening primrose may be the answer – once allergies such as milk, dairy foods and wheat have been ruled out. Tiki vitamin E oil is very soothing and calming for the skin, too. Saturated fats (red meats, lard, butter, bacon and pork) may interfere with the body's production of prostaglandins, which are vital for many of its processes. Margarines (many also contain hydrogenated fat) have been processed in such a way that their linoleic acid is converted into transfatty acid. These are an unhealthy by-product of margarine and interfere with Nature's methods of maintaining bodily health. As a result, blood-cholesterol levels are raised, the immune system is affected, and there can be skin problems. The vitamins B, C and E, zinc, magnesium and selenium are necessary for the body to manufacture its own prostaglandins. Fish oils are an early part of the manufacturing process and will help it along. (These will also protect the child against thrombosis, high cholesterol or menstrual problems at a later age.)

Health

Maybe it is because their 'knees' are always submerged in astrological waters that Capricorns have problems there, and keeping this area warm and dry is important. A build-up of toxins from denatured food can affect the bones and cause twinges and aches, so it is useful for them to try a one-day fruit and mineral water fast once every two weeks. (Not too often, for Capricornians have no fat reserves.) As I have already said, sugar is detrimental to the skeleton: it mobilises calcium which the body then excretes, leaving the bones in a weakened state. Processed food will encourage the material side of the Capricorn nature, as will red meat and alcohol, which interfere with spirituality. If they feel attracted by a vegetarian diet then they should gradually adapt to it. This is a step forward in the fight between the material and the spiritual, of which at times they may be sharply aware. They will have little ammunition with which to defend themselves if they are eating the usual Western diet and drinking alcohol regularly. The vegetarian diet of India is ideal, as long as they make sure that they eat live plain yoghourt daily, take B complex which contains B12, and balance the amino acids at each meal. (See appendix.)

The Capricorn duality can be seen as a fight between light (Amaltheia) and dark (Chronos), and plant foods are full of light. Red meats and Foods from the Dead Zone (see appendix) will stimulate the cold, material half, and are to be avoided as much as possible. The nectar and ambrosia of Amatheia is what is needed – and this can't be found in the flesh of dead animals packed with hormones and antibiotics, nor in refined flour and sugar. Dead Zone foods encourage the physical and emotional stagnation that is at the root of so many Capricornian problems. These create an acid system that breeds toxins and encourages rheumatism and arthritis. When my Capricorn father was a meat-eater and coffee-drinker, he suffered from years of indigestion and chronic sneezing bouts, (the body's attempt to expel toxins). He eventually contracted crippling gout. As by then he had a basically healthy diet, and believing in self-help, he refused his physician's offer of a lifetime on anti-gout pills and rectified his diet. He also began taking very long, brisk walks each day. Now in his seventy-fifth year, he can outwalk the younger members of the family and has not had so much as a twinge of gout in ten years. Who can say how it would have turned out had he stayed on the diet that was literally poisoning him, while taking medication that would have been adding to the damage?

Capricorn is one of the long-lived signs, and fitness is not difficult to attain as this is a naturally active sign. There will always be a welcome routine to keep these subjects occupied – unless they are overcome by depression. The Bach flower remedy Mustard can be helpful with these black moods, and this is one of Nature's remedies. A calcium-rich diet is important, too, for bones and teeth; and beta-carotene is vital for skin and tissues. (Beta-carotene is the precursor of vitamin A.) The coldness of Saturn will make them eager sun-seekers but they should always protect themselves with sun creams, natural beta-carotene, and after-sun lotions. Capricorn skin may be extremely dry or rough, and honey-based creams and moisturisers are useful for this, as is Tiki vitamin E oil. For psoriasis, oily fish and fish oils are highly recommended and can have dramatic results. Oil of evening primrose may also be helpful. There is an excellent range of lotions for men that are cruelty free. Most commercial ones are likely to have been tested on animals, especially if they have 'new' on the label.

Capricorns can have teeth like fortresses, but can be as prone to gum disease as anyone. To keep those gums healthy, they should floss, then brush at night with equal quantities of salt and baking soda, and rub on tincture of myrrh to tone and strengthen the gums. A high-fibre diet of crunchy raw fruits and vegetables will massage the gums, and daily vitamin C protects them. If there is bleeding or swelling, brush twice a day with the above mixture or swill the mouth with a salt mouthwash if unable to brush. Parodontax is a toothpaste that combines all the protective elements and this can also be rubbed around the bases of the teeth.

If they absolutely must have meat, then fowl is the healthiest – and should be from free-range birds that have had the chance to soak up sunshine and fresh air and been allowed to scratch happily in the grit and earth. Stressed animals cause digestive upsets when eaten – especially for the sluggish Saturnian system that is hampered by its sea-bound half.

That is also where the bottled-up emotions are, and these too can cause digestive upsets if not released. Writing may help release them; meditation certainly will. Letting off steam is important, but most Capricorns only do this in familiar company where they feel safe. Acting zany, being silly and idiotic can work wonders as a safety valve. Unfortunately, many of this sign can only do that when they have had a few drinks, which leads them to think of alcohol as a blissful release. Using stimulants to obtain the desired effect is not wise; it is cheating. People are out of control when they have drunk too much alcohol – which may be very enticing for Capricorns, who are so much in control the rest of the time, but they learn nothing from this easy method. Anyone can do this. They want to be special. If they can't be zany in front of people, then they should do it in private for the time being, or go dancing, so that tensions can be released to music. Playing powerful dramatic music at home can let their souls soar.

Long work periods should be broken by a complete change of mood. Half an hour of music and meditation, deep breathing in the fresh air, reading something entirely separate from work, or a short, brisk walk if they can get outside. Fresh air is best if it can be found. Air conditioning, with its closed windows is one of the nastiest tricks ever played on human beings. It shuts out not only fresh air but the beneficial light and Earth magnetism which is vital for health. If forced to breathe this recycled air, an ionisier for the office is advisable – especially for those using computers. Capricorns should have some greenery nearby, too, and every time that they tend it, think of their submerged half, awash in water just like the plant. Water is the symbol of the unconscious mind and it will help them to grow strong along with their plant if they reflect on their subconscious at these times. Every time the plant puts out a feeler or grows a bud, they will know that they are developing emotionally, too. If they have bad luck with their plant and it dies, then they know that the so-called air conditioning is not good for their health, and should buy that ioniser and get another plant. If they take it home with them at weekends, it will be a reminder not to neglect their emotions. The regular habit of caring for a plant will establish a regular habit of acknowledging and freeing those bottled-up, submerged feelings before they develop into full-scale depression.

Herbal teas for Capricorn

Apple tea and fresh apple juice (diluted with water) for rheumatic complaints. Dandelion coffee to stimulate liver and kidneys into expelling toxins which can accumulate and make the system acid. Parsley tea, made from the dried root, for rheumatism and arthritis. Cherries and freshly made cherry tea are excellent for gout and related complaints. All the above will, by aiding the expulsion of toxins, help the skin.

11

AQUARIUS

The astrological world view permeated much of European culture . . .
painting, literature, music, architecture. Many of the great Gothic cathedrals were constructed according to planetary principles based on Pythagorean numerology, the last example being King's College Chapel, Cambridge.

Nicholas Campion, historian and astrologer

Even in 7th century England it was the custom to arrange medical treatment according to the phases of the Moon.

Nicholas Campion

Aquarius the Water Carrier: c. 20 January–c. 19 February   Planetary rulers: Uranus and Saturn. Element: Air. Physical rulership: ankles, circulation, shins. By polarity with Leo: the heart.

Destiny of Aquarius: to champion those in need (and do less talking).

Herbs for Aquarius: for rheumatism, those recommended for Capricorn. Dandelion to purify the blood, tone the liver and kidneys. Nettle for the circulation.

Vital vitamins and minerals for Aquarius: vitamins C and E for the circulation and heart. Calcium for strong bones. Lecithin to keep the arteries free flowing.

Gems for Aquarius: green-blue turquoise, which was

believed to protect its wearer by soaking up any evil vibrations that came near them. It is also fruitful for meditation purposes and is associated with a tranquil mind.

The myth behind the motivation

From the myth of Uranus (Ouranos; heaven; sky) we see how good can come of evil. The marriage of Heaven (Uranus) and Earth (Gaia) was not without its problems. Gaia produced so many monstrous children that Uranus banished some of them (the Cyclops) to the Underworld. Being far from happy about this, Gaia sharpened a sickle. Her youngest son, Chronos, stepped forward to take it from her hands. With it, he castrated Uranus and took over the work of procreation for himself. From Uranus's spilt blood were born the Titans, the mighty ones, and Aphrodite, Goddess of Love.

This sounds a gory tale of mayhem, and yet Uranian sacrifices have been producing love and strength for humankind for centuries. If Aquarians can put aside their own desires, their vanity, their sense of self-importance, then they can spread love and light in the most magical way.

Until the discovery of Uranus in 1781, Aquarians were ruled by Saturn (Chronos), and there are still Saturnian Aquarians around. If they read the entry for Capricorn, they will learn more about themselves. Physically, they are small-boned, dark-haired and with dark or greenish-hazel eyes. Their skin will be sallow and tan easily. Their teeth will be strong but on the yellowish side, their hair lacking shine. They may have some physical imbalance. They will be people who take life seriously, work hard, and do not smile easily. Like Capricorns, they are comfortable working to the clock. One Capricorn I know, when asked if he is hungry, always looks at his watch before he replies.

Modern Aquarians, who are very much Uranus ruled, have for their symbol the Water Carrier. The water can be beneficial, nourishing and fertilising; or it can be black and poisoned. Where self-seeking and self-aggrandisement are uppermost, the water will be a poisonous brew. Radical politics often feature in Aquarian lives; they love to shock and startle, and this can spring from a mischevous sense of fun or a malicious desire to create havoc. Adrian Edmondson of the Young Ones was born under this sign. So too are Bernie Grant, John Liden (ex-Johnny Rotten of the Sex Pistols), Ozzy Osbourne and Alice Cooper. Aquarians Mary Quant and Bill Gibb created the very Aquarian fashion revolution in the Britain of the sixties.

Subjects of this sign may create disorder and anarchy with the objective of fashioning a new order, as did Chronos, but this is all too often the kind of order that they themselves feel to be right. Their beliefs can be all-mighty (this is a Fixed Sign) and they can be immovable. They know that they are right, just as Chronos knew that he was right when he dethroned his father. Sometimes, for their own good, they need cutting down (figuratively speaking, of course) before they do the cutting.

It is better if Aquarians put their own houses in order where possible, before any external weapon sweeps down and deprives them of everything they most cherish. If it is poisoned water that they choose to pour out around them then they must remember that the poison may affect them, too. The brotherhood of man (or, more properly, humankind) is their special sphere, and here they can provide original ideas and energies that will extensively benefit the world; but, without a proper cause, the Uranian energies can be frittered away on the perverse and disturbing.

Some of the Aquarian's ideas will be unworkable or even impossible, but some will be brilliant. Their urge to help may override everything else; they may put aside family, friends, loved ones, in pursuit of their burning causes, as did Chronos. They may look and behave 'spaced out' when obsessed with a new plan or project. Without these individual thinkers and originators, the world would be a dreary place, but we have to remind ourselves continually of this when they are at their most eccentric! They can be the lightning flash that dazzles our lives – the lightning that comes out of the blue from the heavens they rule – or they can be the shock that knocks us off our feet and from which we think we shall never recover.

In ancient times, water was a blessing from the gods. Mohammed, when asked what was the greatest gift anyone could give, replied, 'Water'. We in our water-bound Western land find it difficult to envisage what this liquid meant to a world that was frequently parched and arid. Water gods proliferated in the ancient world. There was Ea, the Babylonian God of Wisdom and the Magical Arts. He poured out sweet water upon the world, and his portraits show him surrounded by watery waves which resemble the wavy glyph for Aquarius. When the Hittites adopted him as their god, they called him the Keeper of the Tablets of Destiny and regarded him as the wisest counsellor. Aquarians are frequently in positions where they give good advice – it may simply be as an interested friend, or more likely as a trained counsellor or skilled hypnotherapist (Sue Washington, one of Britain's top hypnotherapists, is an Aquarian). They may be involved in unusual or intriguing research, or be imaginative, creative writers of fantasy or science fiction. (Keith Timson, author of the *Saga of the Disenchanted* series; Jules Verne; Philip José Farmer, author of the *Riverworld* series, first wrote of love affairs between aliens and humans – a very Aquarian subject; SF writers and editors Thomas M. Disch, Judy-Lynn del Rey and Terry Carr were born under this sign. Aquarian Lewis Carroll wrote the most Uranian book ever created: *Alice in Wonderland*. Iain Banks's books are emphatically Uranian at its most strange, bizarre and disturbing. Sir Thomas More was a great Aquarian idealist who wrote of Utopia. (Displaying the rigidity of the Fixed Sign, he went to the block rather than change his views.)

The Uranian Aquarian is small-boned, of medium height, slim, and as this is the sign of the unexpected, their eyes may be an eldritch green, speckled hazel, or a very bright blue. Their hair may be dark brown, mid-brown or bright gold. High, broad cheekbones and/or a noble Roman nose are two of the features that identify them, but they are not always easy to spot – and may look like another sign entirely! They may have a body that is a little crooked – say, one shoulder higher than the other. The women of the sign have small, white, beautiful hands with the knuckles just a little larger than the finger width. They love to talk, to meet people, to mix socially, but many of them also prefer to be alone at times. Like Sagittarius, they can put their foot in it verbally and speak out of turn, or hurt someone's feelings with a thoughtless phrase. An unhappy Aquarian can have a bitter tongue. There is often something different about this sign, some eccentricity or something odd or unusual. There can also be a cold or chilly air about some of them; or merely a feeling of distance between them and other people. They feel very

uncomfortable about emotional displays, and
frequently try to deny their own emotions.

The Aquarius child

No ordinary child this. Those born under the sign of
Aquarius will be bright and sharp and provide
unusual insights into life and people. Their dreamy
expressions may indicate that they are not taking
things in but their imagination is so rich and powerful
that plenty is happening whether or not others are
aware of it. They will love to paint and draw and
read. They will love the cinema, the theatre, acting,
the arts. The boys won't be self-conscious about
dressing up in girls' clothes for plays and panto-
mimes and fancy-dress parties. The coming of the
Age of Aquarius has brought us many examples of
the androgynous nature of this sign: cross-dressing,
transsexualism, sex-change operations, male pop
stars who dress like women, girls in jeans and men's
shirts. Right back to the severe, mannish haircut
called the Eton crop in the twenties, and women
throwing off the restrictions of the corset, the coming
of the Age of Aquarius was in evidence.

This doesn't mean to say that little Aquarians will
display any of this, but if they do, it is better to
understand that they are not being at all abnormal
for their sign. Their individuality is not something
that should be crushed with ridicule or punishment.
Gentle dissuasion of any public behaviour that is
causing the child problems, and helping them to
understand their own sign (as far as this complex
and sometimes perplexing sign can be understood)
are most beneficial. So is telling them that they have a
special place in the world as counsellors and creators,
innovators and skilful wielders of the modern 'magic'

arts such as the cinema, television and the media. If they want to learn ballet or acting or have their voices coached, they are to be encouraged. Harrassing or pressuring them will drive them away. As they fight to understand themselves as they enter their teens, it is important that parents remain their good, true friends through everything, for they value friendship above all. Sadly, many Aquarian children have parents who will not or cannot understand them, and the divide is unbridgeable. That is not the children's fault.

In the arts, their original thinking and unique ideas can be channelled creatively. They may also wish to do some kind of voluntary or charity work. They will never have to be persuaded to give some of their pocket money to a good cause, but in other ways their careful use of money may be a surprise. They love having friends round for tea; they love having parties. There is a little of Leo, their polar opposites, in them at such times when they play host or hostess with such warmth and charm.

Or they may be quiet and painfully shy and suffer agonies on social occasions. The higher their education, the more likely it is that their future achievements will be remarkable ones, but there are the naturally gifted who will produce imaginative writing and show extraordinary artistic talent out of a hat, as it were. Of course, because their talents can be so different, unusual and innovative, parents and teachers may not see them as such. The coming of the Aquarian Age has brought to the fore such Uranian people as Francis Bacon, the artist whose disturbing and shocking paintings continue to cause a furore; James Joyce, author of *Ulysses*; Carl Jung, psychoanalyst and dream and symbol analyser; Betty Friedan, leader of the women's movement; Germaine Greer, author of *The Female Eunuch*; Angela Davis, radical;

Karl Marx, prophet of so many revolutions; Colette; Vanessa Redgrave; Gertrude Stein and Yoko Ono. Emmeline Pankhurst was Aquarius rising. Aquarians can have a wonderful touch for light comedy (Marti Caine; Farah Fawcett; Carol Channing; Benny Hill) and even when small, they will show a different approach to matters. This can be discouraged (which is a very sad state of affairs) or enjoyed. How boring and tedious life would be without the gifts and talents of Aquarians! Parents should keep this in mind when they find that their youngster has decided to paint the walls direct by throwing tins of paint at them, or has had one of the famous Aquarian outbursts (i.e. one that's stunningly tactless) in front of a guest of honour.

They love truth, and honesty can be their forte – as with Zsa Zsa Gabor, who makes no bones about being a good housekeeper by always keeping the house when she divorces! Isn't it sometimes better to be blunt and outspoken than to be secretly scheming? I'm not saying that parents shouldn't teach their child to practise tact and diplomacy – a rude, tactless child will only be disliked – but they would be wise to avoid suppressing the Uranian individuality, for there's nothing else like it in the world.

Ankles are the Aquarian weak spot, and should be well supported during games and sports. Ice packs (wrapped in a cloth first) should go straight onto sprained ankles, for no longer than twenty minutes at a time. A small bag of frozen peas is ideal. Arnica is the homeopathic remedy for bruises and sprains, and this cream should be in the Aquarian medicine cabinet. A homeopath can be consulted if the damage is more serious. Rest is essential. Trying to walk on a damaged ankle can strain the spine and stress the body. Comfrey ointment is valuable too – and comfrey pills to aid the mending of a broken or frac-

tured bone. (Comfrey's old name is knitbone.) The
high-fibre diet is protective as children get older
(babies and infants have different diet needs and
should not be given extra bran) and will give a good
basic support for the circulatory and cardiac system.
Brightly coloured raw vegetables cut into interesting
shapes are a good way of starting a child on the road
to health, and there should always be a dish or two
of these on the table. A few mouthfuls of raw food
to start every meal will prevent the body from setting
up barriers to cooked food, which it treats as an
invader. It's quite likely that the Aquarian child will
want to become vegetarian, for this sign has an
affinity with all living creatures and finds the thought
of eating animal flesh abhorrent. It also smacks of
the strong being merciless to the weak, which is
anathama to them.

The vegetarian diet, if properly handled, is healthy
and energy-giving. Although there is thought to be
the danger of a shortage of B12, this rarely shows up
in blood tests. Live plain yoghourt daily will help to
build this vitamin, and teenage girls whose periods
have begun should have plenty of alfalfa sprouts,
dried fruits, black molasses, kelp, free range egg
yolks, dark green vegetables, brewer's yeast, wheatgerm and wholegrain cereals. If anaemia presents
itself, chelated iron tablets are best, for they do not
upset the system. Inorganic iron (many iron tonics
come in this form) destroys vitamin E, and they
should not be taken within eight hours of each other.
Iron can be taken in the morning and vitamin E in
the evening, or vice versa. Vitamin C helps to assimi-
late iron, so taking unsweetened fruit juice, a fresh
orange, or a vitamin C tablet with the pills or tonic
is a sensible idea.

Shy young Aquarians may suffer agonies of
tension and stress in social situations, and the Bach

flower remedy Larch will build up their confidence. For panic attacks, they can try Bach's Rock Rose. They will like the idea of taking a natural remedy that has not been tested on animals. I hope that they won't be denied pets, for dogs or cats that they can hug will help them to overcome their shyness and diffidence. They will enjoy practising unusual methods of overcoming stress, too, such as t'ai chi, meditation, yoga or chanting. They love all that is new and novel, so parents should not have difficulty finding the method that suits their children. When their tensions build up unbearably, Aquarians can present a very cold face to the world and fool everybody into thinking that they are unfeeling; or they may fool people with jokes and smiles that conceal the unhappiness beneath. Sometimes they get stuck in a rut and, seeing no way out of it, they plod on when they should be taking quite another route. That is where a parent's gentle guidance can be invaluable.

This strange mixture of shyness, lack of confidence, tactlessness, wilfulness and stubbornness is how the Aquarian child should be. There's nothing wrong there. Uranus is a unique planet and it produces unique offspring. Parents may marvel at everything they do, or consider them the black sheep of the family, but with an Aquarian they'll never be bored!

Health

Their zest for life generally keeps Aquarians extremely fit and full of bounce, but they may have periods of total exhaustion as a result of overdoing it. Being positive (like Aries) that nothing could ever harm them and that their health is invincible, they

may indulge in harmful or weird habits. Heavy
smoking and sugar consumption seems out of place
for this sign, and yet one of the heaviest smokers
and sugar consumers I know has Aquarius rising.
Another example of the unexpected! A high-fibre diet
is essential to protect the circulatory system and
heart, and a well-balanced vegetarian regime
supplies this nicely. Wholegrains, raw vegetables,
fresh fruit, wheatgerm and sunflower seeds are all
heart and circulation protectors. Vitamins E and B
complex are essential, too, along with vitamins C and
B6. Oily fish at least twice a week is the premier heart
insurance available, and this can be supplemented
with halibut or cod-liver oil capsules. Saturated fats
should be avoided, as should hydrogenated fat (often
added to so-called 'healthy' margarines). High cholesterol levels can be lowered by eating oatmeal and
oats twice daily, and taking polyunsaturated fatty
acids (variously called Vitamin F, PUFA and EFA),
which come in seed and vegetable oils. The richest
sources of linoleic acid are oils made from evening
primrose, safflower, corn or maize, wheatgerm,
peanut and olive. (Always ensure that your oils are
cold-pressed, for heating and processing destroys
their nutrients and their protective qualities.)

Aquarian ankles and shins need total dietary
support, and this comes from plenty of sunlight and
foods rich in vitamin D, which helps the absorption
of calcium. These foods are kippers, mackerel,
canned salmon, sardines – also tuna, but as catching
this fish usually involves the violent death of many
dolphins, most animal-lovers would wish to avoid it
– eggs and cows' milk. Calcium-rich foods include
milk, cheese, molasses, potatoes, dried figs, cauli-
flowers, broccoli, legumes and green, leafy
vegetables. Levels of phosphorus are high in junk
food and canned fizzy drinks, and this increases the

body's calcium needs, which are unlikely to be met with such poor nutrition. The result is weakened bones and teeth. Unleavened bread such as chapattis should also be avoided as they contain phytates, which obstruct the absorption of calcium. When bread has risen, the danger is removed.

Prolonged bed rest also weakens the bones, and if there is an allergy to cow's milk or the lactose it contains, this will further affect calcium absorption. It is important that Aquarians are relaxed at meal-times, that they chew thoroughly and do not gulp down their food and then rush away. Tension and haste obstruct digestion and this can lead to calcium loss. Walking and all weight-bearing exercise strengthen the bones. Sugar mobilises calcium and encourages osteoporosis; it also increases nervousness and dramatically alters blood-sugar levels – none of which improves the Aquarian moods! If calcium is not being properly absorbed for one reason or another, then a supplement of hydrochloric acid will help, for without this in plentiful supply in the stomach, digestion is inefficient.

Herbal teas for Aquarius

This is a sign that likes to try anything new and unusual, and Ruby Red by Floradix may well prove to be a favourite, along with Jill Davies' China Light and Jamaica Spice. When feeling strained, chamomile is a soothing relaxer.

12

PISCES

We, each of us, have to get away from
bargaining for love and security. Then
we will enjoy it continuously.

Roy Gillett

Water is the vehicle of the power of the
Goddess; but equally, it is She who
personifies the mystery of the waters of
birth and dissolution – whether of the
individual or of the universe.

Joseph Campbell

Pisces the Fishes: c. 20 February–c. 20 March
Planetary ruler: Neptune. Element: Water. Physical
rulership: the feet, lymphatic system, body fluids. By
polarity with Virgo: the duodenum.

Destiny of Pisces: to enchant and delight; to refuse to
evade reality when doing so may harm others.

Herbs for Pisces: kelp, for healthy blood; echinacea
and blue flag root for lymphatic cleansing; marjoram
and parsley root for water retention.

Vital vitamins and minerals for Pisces: vitamins C, E,
B complex, to maintain the health of the lymphatic
(immune) system, along with essential fatty acids.
Zinc and iron are major immune supporters, but
should not be taken together.

Gems for Pisces: pale blue sapphire; aquamarine; opal;
pale green emerald. Piscean Elizabeth Taylor has
made the diamond representative of this sign. After

all, it is the colour of clear water. One sixteenth-century book proclaims that diamonds 'are to resist poyson and witchecraft; to put away feare, to give victorie in contention, to helpe them that be lunatike or phrantike.' Certainly, in putting away fear they will be helpful to the Piscean. Sapphires will encourage tranquillity, innocence and delight, and attract good friends.

The myth behind the motivation

Fish gods and goddesses abounded in the days that were considered not so far removed from the burgeoning waters of Earth's creation. Atargatis was worshipped in mermaid form in Ascalon, where fish and doves were sacred to her. Her name is a composite of Astarte (whose doves she adopted) and Anat, and she was Mother Goddess to the Syrians, who considered her the source of all fertility. Dagon was a Semitic Corn God whose name was wrongly thought by the Israelites to mean fish, so they portrayed him with a fish's tail. Father of Baal, he is mentioned in the Bible (*Judges* 16:23) in the most reverent tones as the premier Philistine deity. The Mayan and Toltec god, Kukulkan, was symbolised by a fish in his form of God of Water. He was also God of Reincarnation and Resurrection.

Humankind was born in the dark mysterious water of creation, and to these we periodically return, tossed like fish in the fathomless deep, with very few of us suspecting the truth in the secretive, self-deceiving world of Neptune.

Neptune/Poseidon was God of the Sea and of Earthquakes. Having lived through a minor earthquake, I believe I know why. The thunderous sound that an earthquake makes is like the thudding of thousands of hooves, and Poseidon was God of Horses and Bulls. Borne in a chariot drawn by dolphins or sea horses, he carried a trident in his hand. His gift to humankind was the horse, and in the Roman festivals in his honour, richly caparisoned horses were decked with flowers and led through the streets. Neptune was as prolific in his love affairs as Zeus, and by changing himself into many forms he sired many children. He became a horse so that he could court Ceres (Demeter, Harvest Queen), and a river to woo Tyro. To hide Theophane from her suitors, he changed her into a sheep while he himself took on the form of a ram. The offspring of their union was the legendary ram with the golden fleece.

Pisceans come in many forms. They can be delightful angel fish, sleek and beautiful, a pleasure to watch; or predatory, smiling sharks, their objective the destruction of their rivals, or imagined rivals. They can be slippery, evasive eels; or friendly trout that enjoy being tickled under the chin. There are fabulous fish that bedazzle the eye (Cleopatra); and shy, retiring fish that like to hide amongst the shadowy coral in the dark depths of the ocean. There are those who flit through the waters of life light-heartedly and without a backward thought for those they have deceived or left behind; and there are generous, protective fish that allow others to feed off them or be shielded by them (the Duchess of Kent). There is often some mystery, secret or deception about Pisceans . . . B. Traven, the mysterious writer of *Treasure of the Sierra Madre* was a Pisces. So was Merle Oberon, who kept her true origins totally hidden. Tom Keating, who painted brilliant copies of famous works of art, deceiving art lovers for years, was born under this sign, as was Scientology founder L. Ron Hubbard. The French Foreign Legion was formed under Pisces, its soldiers adopting a new identity on joining, their pasts remaining secret, their new way of life an itinerant one. Even when highly gifted, Pisceans sometimes waste their talents, by disorganisation, laziness, procrastination, or simply that fleeting lack of continuity of thought and purpose that is so obvious in the many flitting movements of a fish. Kenneth Grahame employed Piscean talent to excellent use in his famous classic, *Wind in the Willows*, with Ratty the water rat, Toad of Toad Hall, and Mole, romping in and out of the river. Harry Harrison, author of the *Stainless Steel Rat* series, has as his main character the amoral Slippery Jim, who is renowned for his ingenious escapades. (Try keeping hold of a wriggling fish!)

Because this is the sign of self-deception, the more negative Pisceans may think that they are living worthwhile lives whereas, in fact, they are wasting themselves. So much passes through the minds of negative Pisceans as if borne along on ever flowing currents that they cannot grasp at one continuing thought and build on it. In the morning they might think that they will be great artists; by evening, they have decided that they don't have the energy. The day after, they want to write poetry; next day, it is music that attracts them. They may be convinced that they are exceptionally talented, but not prepared to give any effort to their dream-ambitions.

How can they have a sense of time when they are water-borne, when they swim through the mysterious depths of the unconscious? What is time? It means nothing to them; it can be nothing to them. As if they are still in the waters of the womb, they feel protected, safe and hidden away from harm. Nothing can damage them, not even alcohol, not even drugs, not even their own stupidity. The light always shines ahead for them, where others would be able to perceive and avoid the darkness. Piscean

Andy Gibb was one of those who was unable to beat his drug habit, as was Rolling Stone Brian Jones. Piscean author Jack Kerouac actually advocated a life of drugs, drink and self-indulgence in *On the Road* (and died young of drink). Pisceans Elizabeth Taylor and Liza Minnelli have fortunately been able to conquer their addictions, and it was because of drugs prescribed for back pain that Elizabeth Taylor became the victim of dependency. Even aspirin can be too much for the delicate Neptunian system.

When those with Neptune in Libra (born between late 1942 and 1955) were old enough to make an impression on the world, they made it with flower power and the peace movement, psychedelic drugs and harmony and kisses. Music and flowing robes, and the mystic East (also Libra-ruled) came to the fore, and there were songs of love and brotherhood and against war. At its worst, Neptune in Libra allows those possessing it to destroy themselves with drugs and alcohol while believing that they are making an enormous contribution to humankind, or alternately they may begin the drug habit because they believe that the world is such a terrible place they cannot face it. Neptune in Libra at its best brought us great creative artists who filled our lives with brilliant and colourful fantasy, David Bowie being a prime example.

Neptune fashions a beautiful illusion, seduces its unsuspecting victims and conquers them. If the union is fruitful, if other, stronger qualities in the birthchart bring determination and application, then a golden fleece might be the result. If not, then there might well be a sad waste of talent. Wanting an easy way, believing that there is an easy way, is typically Neptunian. Neptune himself had a poor talent for arguing, and this is what one would expect of the darting fish that cannot keep to its course. Those who love to tell a rambling tale (Frankie Howard, Jasper Carrott, Rik Mayall) are Piscean-born – and so is famous mime artist Marcel Marceau, who, like the fish, speaks not at all and glides through the air without a sound, using his arms like fins. The two greatest male ballet dancers of all time, Nijinsky and Rudolf Nureyev, were both born under this sign, (the Pisces feet can be superb at dancing), but Nureyev owes his majestic stage presence and belief in himself to his Leo ascendant.

Physically, Pisceans can be slender as eels or round as plaice. Their hair is black, their skins usually fair. Their eyes are either huge and round, or protuberant, their colour that of the sea, blue-green, blue-grey, deep blue or crystal pale. Piscean women often have a girlish, tender, vulnerable look about them (Patsy Kensit, Jennifer Jones, Lesley-Ann Down) and their eyes are limpid, their loveliness radiant when they are beautiful. The Piscean mouth is sometimes round, or blobby, not unlike that of a fish, or a thin gash, again like that of a fish. Michael Caine has the protuberant Pisces eyes. Because fish have no voices, this is not a singing sign, and sometimes the voice can be small, or sound rather strangled. (Liza Minelli has Taurus rising, from whence she gets her powerful voice.) The feet may be noticeable, either spread wide when walking, like flippers, or bare (Sandie Shaw). Piscean women like to paint their toe nails bright colours, and they do not usually have good legs, for their ankles are thick. (Imagine the ankles pressed together and you will see a mermaid's tail, thick at the base.) Their eyes soon brim with emotion, and they have tender hearts. Animals will captivate them. Sometimes the men of the sign may have a distinctly undersea appearance that reminds one of a fish-like character in *Stingray*, with oddly bulging eyes and flat little nose. There is also a long,

melancholy face seen with this sign, and there may
be shyness and a desire for seclusion, as with their
polar opposites, Virgo.

The Pisces child

Piscean children should never be punished for not
telling the truth. They may not be capable of doing
so, and they may not even perceive what truth is.
Lost in a baffling world of fantasy, imagination and
intuitive perception, these children may believe that
they know what is right and what is wrong, but do
they? They can be awfully wrong while being positive that they are right. When one lives in such a
Neptune-ruled metier, suspicion breeds. Did I think
that, or did they deceive me into thinking that I did?
They must be cunning; they must be trying to trick
me! – is typical Piscean reasoning. The most primitive
instincts blossom in such a mental state: they are
needed for survival.

This, of course, is Pisces at its most negative. There
are wonderful, warm-hearted Pisceans who care
deeply for others and have compassionate hearts.
They will weep over sad happenings and can't bear
to sit through tragic films or television. They cannot
stand seeing proof of man's inhumanity to humankind. Hiding away is sometimes the only way that
they can survive such a bitter, cruel world, where
pain and suffering lie round every corner. Like the
wary fish that conceals itself in the deep-sea shadows
to evade the hungry predator, the Pisces child will
shrink from unpleasantness. Some children will cling
avidly to religion for their support; others will
consider that atheism is the only possible course in
such a God-forsaken world, for how could a loving
God allow such terrible things to happen?

Most of all they need their parents' loving and continuing support if they are to grow up with some modicum of confidence and courage. They need family there to love and shield them – but overdoing this will make matters worse. They need to understand that they must stand on their own feet like any other children; they must learn the ways of life, cruel though they sometimes are, and that everyday ups and downs are all part and parcel of it. It can be a terrible disappointment if they are so protected that they think they are here solely to find the crock of gold at the end of the rainbow. Life can be hard. It can be painful. We are here to learn, not to flit away our days in idle and vapid entertainment. Raising them to be confident in themselves, to know that they have an important role to play, will make them much happier. They should be encouraged in a regular routine while they are small, because it is routine and timekeeping that Pisces find so difficult to learn. If they are introduced to gentle herbs, they will reach for chamomile or valerian – instead of more harmful drugs – when things get too painful for them. Neptunians are extremely sensitive to drugs of all kinds; they should be taught that the natural way is always best for them. I know a Piscean who sinks into sleep on one aspirin, who gave up cigarettes because one puff made her dizzy, who sticks to mineral water because even a sip of alcohol knocks her out. They can be that susceptible. So are those with Neptune in the sixth house (the house of health), or with Neptune rising.

The Piscean child will sometimes be unbearably intuitive, feeling and sensing anguish where people are striving to hide it, weeping over others' despair, others' misfortunes. This does no one any good, of course, but they cannot help it. That is how they are, and parents and teachers have to accept it. Floods of tears are part of the Piscean existence, especially in childhood, and as tears are always better out than in it would be unwise to try and suppress them. It is unwise too to tell them that they are stupid for crying; or to tell a Piscean boy that 'men do not cry'. Piscean men do; they have profound feelings; that is how they were made, and no one should interfere with it. The opposite is, of course, the uncaring cold fish. No one would want them to be like that instead. But if they are made ashamed or scared of their own feelings, they will abhor any such display in others.

Piscean children should never turn out for sports in bare feet and they should not be allowed to get their feet damp and cold, for damp can get into their body this way. Six glasses of mineral water a day will keep their kidneys functioning and help to prevent an excess storage of body fluids. Artificially coloured and flavoured drinks will upset them. Swimming, needless to say, is a supreme exercise for them, and they will love water in all its forms. (But don't let's be overenthusiastic. Pisces boys are as unlikely to enjoy washing as boys of any other sign!) Music and dance, aerobics and t'ai chi should appeal, as will anything gentle and artistic. Soft pastel colours will soothe them: gentle sea greens and blues, tender mauve pinks and turquoises. With plants and flowers to surround them, and a tank of fish to entertain and relax them, they should be happy. They are not material children; they do not need oceans of toys to keep them amused, nor do they covet their friends' possessions. Love and tenderness is what they need, for they have a romantic attitude to life. They can be so desperately hurt by their early dabblings with the opposite sex that they shy away from future entanglements, or be so eager to please their parents and so afraid of facing their anger that they forfeit their own happiness (as Elizabeth Barrett Browning did for many years).

The cinema is ruled by Neptune, and these are the children who will adore playing parts on stage, dressing up and pretending to be princes and princesses and fabulous creatures of legend and renown. With them, it is not the ego of Leo that drives them or the sheer pressure of artistic energy of Libra, but the desire to assume many roles and play many parts. While they are doing this, they can hide themselves, for all eyes will be upon the character they are playing and not upon them. They can assume many roles one after the other, or play a very Piscean role like that of the trusting, ever-willing-to-be-conned bodyguard of Arthur Daley, as Dennis Waterman does in *Minder*. The harmony and beauty of the ballet may attract them from a young age, if they can tolerate the disciplines. Some legendary dancing feet belong to this sign (Cyd Charisse, Nureyev, Nijinsky).

The compassionate, tender-hearted Pisceans can be too trusting and very naïve in their belief in the goodwill and honesty of others. Teaching them caution, common sense with money and the rudiments of business acumen is vital.

They need cuddly pets as well as the obligatory goldfish, to have warm furry bundles to hold. Parents should encourage them in all their interests and enthuse over their paintings and poetry, their acting roles. They may well feel inadequate because they think they can offer little practical everyday assistance, and if this is the case then it is up to parents to let them know that their loving, gentle hearts and artistic gifts fill their lives with a magic that no one else can supply. Their Capricorn, Taurus and Virgo brothers and sisters will offer the practical help. They will provide the enchantment.

Dreams will interest them and help them to understand themselves and it would be of assistance if a parent learned something of dream interpretation and passed this on. My Piscean mother always used to discuss her dreams with me, and that is how I became interested in symbolism. She took me to the ballet; she first interested me in astrology. She came from a family that thought astrology was just so much nonsense. They tried to discourage her, but she wisely refused to listen. Pisceans can be very stubborn, but they can just as easily be swayed, persuaded to give up what they love – and that is very sad. Piscean children need to be taught to have the courage of their convictions and to stand by what they believe in.

Should they feel that life is too harsh or painful, they may adopt symptoms of illness, real or imagined, as a retreat, and this needs a sensible response. If they are already feeling beleaguered, then they cannot be bullied into a swift recovery. Also, the symptoms might well be real. Pampering them while they are unwell could encourage a habit of retreat into illness; a better response is behaving calmly, talking confidently of how soon the illness will be gone, and reacting with sensible remedies, preferably of the old-fashioned variety. Bach flower remedies are ideal for Pisceans. They need gentle, natural cures.

Health

The Piscean need to be near water is no idle whim. Water is their métier, and this need is as vital as the Taurean one to cultivate the Earth. They will gain a deep spiritual rejuvenation from the sea, from walking or holidaying by it if they cannot live by it.

Yachting, swimming or fishing is balm to their souls. Meandering along a beach, staring into rock pools and collecting unusual shells is a marvellous way for them to forget the pressing problems of the world.

Drinking spring water daily will bring to them all the healing qualities of their element and help to prevent the fluid retention that can plague them. Six glasses a day should be ample. Fibrous foods help to keep the system free of toxins and the blood flowing freely. Kelp in tablet form, or one of the many forms of kelp that can be cooked in various ways, will keep the body working smoothly. Swimming is an ideal exercise, but brisk walking will rid the body of impurities and tone up the feet. Reflexology should appeal, and dancing once or twice a week is an old-fashioned but efficient way of maintaining a healthy body weight.

The whimsical Piscean may begin starvation diets, or decide that an all-fluid diet will cure overweight problems, but low-calorie diets should be avoided for they will encourage the very fluid retention that needs to be avoided. They should always take extra multivitamins when dieting, and never cut the calories too low. The fruit fast is excellent – choosing one type of fruit for each meal and eating as much as required. So is drinking mineral water, unsweetened fruit juice (half and half with water), bouillon, marmite or vegetable juices in between. (Freshly pressed is always best.) There are some excellent books on fasting safely (Leslie Kenton's are highly recommended, see reading list) but generally one day a week is enough. This should be a peaceful day of rest at home without having to rush anywhere or work hard. When fasting, there may be a feeling of nausea or slight headache towards evening. Resting and doing some relaxation exercises as the poisons flow out alleviates this. The worse the symptoms, the more the cleansing is needed. There will be such a feeling of exuberance and achievement next day that the discomfort will have been worth it. A properly completed fast day will give the confidence to beat the perils of gorging and bingeing. Pisceans may find it impossible to stick to a diet for longer than a day or so, which makes the occasional one-day fruit fast a very useful tool for them. Alternatively, there is the potassium day, eating vegetable soups only and drinking mineral water and fruit juices.

Foot problems can respond speedily to homeopathic creams, for instance, massaging with *rhus tox* for sprains or twists, arnica for bruising, calendula for itches, rashes and tough areas. A comfrey leaf or cabbage leaf poultice applied at night is soothing for painful bunions. It does not need to be said that squeezing the feet into tight or unsuitable shoes will only create further problems. Pisceans often like to go barefoot if possible, and this will tone up their feet, but they must not play sports in bare feet. Vitamin E oil by Tiki works quickly on rough skin and the Body Shop makes luscious foot creams. Pisceans may never have thought of giving their feet a face pack, but it can keep them soft and fresh, and if their feet feel good then so do they. They should use a face pack for dry skin, first having washed and massaged the feet to get the circulation flowing; then rest with the feet higher than the head until it is time to remove the pack with warm water, and finish by splashing with cold. If there is no time for this, then setting the shower spray to cold and drenching feet, ankles and calves for a few minutes will tone up the body beautifully.

The right balance of potassium and sodium is vital for a normal balance of body fluids. Eating salted foods and adding salt to dishes is one way of upsetting the balance. Sea salt, which has not been stripped of its natural iodine, is preferable – or a homeopathically balanced table salt such as Biosalt. Foods contain their own natural salt and it is better to enjoy their unadulterated flavours without adding more. Junk foods contain high percentages of sodium and should be avoided. Vegetables should be lightly cooked in a small amount of water and the water then added to soups or stews, or drunk. Steeping, soaking and boiling vegetables destroys their vitamin content and leaches out potassium. Wholegrains, wheatgerm, seeds and nuts, lentils, kidney beans, brewer's yeast, fruit juices, cider vinegar, rice, peas, cabbage and fish all contain potassium. Fish is the ideal diet for Pisceans. It is low-calorie, sympathetic and full of iodine and potassium. (To be avoided, of course, if there is an allergy.)

Restful mealtimes are as important for Pisceans as for their polar opposites, Virgo. Meals should not be rushed or snatched from packets. Television dinners are devoid of healthy, living enzymes and in the main are Foods from the Dead Zone (see appendix). Too much cooked food clogs up the body and causes an eventual build-up of toxins that creates a sluggish system. Vitamin C is one of the major bodily defenders against infection and an ample supply of this daily (it cannot be stored by the body) will support the lymph glands in their work of fighting off infection. When under stress, the lymph glands or nodes swell and become tender to the touch. A vital part of the body's immune system, they fend off invaders, filter out nasty bugs and are very sensitive to nutritional deficiencies. How can they fight infection if they are not fit and healthy themselves? The vitamin defenders that support the immune system are as follows: vitamins A and C, B complex (particularly B5 and B6), vitamin E, folic acid, EFAs (essential fatty acids), selenium, germanium, with iron and zinc being the two main minerals involved. Without sufficient iron, there is a great vulnerability to infection, but an excess of iron can actually depress the immune system.

Foods that harm or weaken the immune system include sugar (this devitalises the immune system); alcohol (this strips the body of the B vitamins and zinc); tobacco (smokers often have a high level of white cells in their blood but this is not protective; it is a sign that they have a chest infection such as bronchitis). Also unhelpful or dangerous to the immune system are overcooked, refined, processed and denatured foods; drinks such as fizzy colas that upset the body's mineral balance; coffee and strong tea (caffeine affects the blood-sugar levels so the body is constantly under stress); antibiotics; immunisation; drug treatment; drug addiction; steroids such as the Pill.

One of the main problems with sugar is that it is filling and satisfies the sweet tooth without doing one iota of good to the body. High-calorie, it causes immediate cravings and addictions which upset the body's ability to know what is good for it. Eating chocolate can cause an immediate craving for a cup of tea; sweets create a thirst for soft drinks, and so on. Short fruit fasts strengthen the immune system, but they must be carried out sensibly. Rushing about while living on air will do more harm than good.

Foods that help to strengthen the immune system include live plain yoghourt, olive oil, acidophilus, garlic (the first taste can be off-putting but you soon adapt to it), raw fresh vegetables, oatmeal, fresh seeds and sprouted seeds, fresh, green, leafy vegetables and fresh fruits. I repeat that alcohol is a poison to the vulnerable Piscean: it destroys vitamins, weakens resistance to infection and destroys this sign's tenuous contact with reality. It is wiser to keep to a maintenance dose of vitamin C, especially if driving or living near a road or industrial area. All pollution destroys vitamin C. And a word of warning: never stop taking it suddenly. If you must stop, then tail off gradually. Oranges are assumed to contain this vitamin, but in a test carried out on oranges from a supermarket, little or no vitamin C was found, so it is better not to rely on fruit for a supply unless picked fresh that day. It is the most easily destroyed vitamin, and when you think of fruit lying baking in sunshine and then being stored for long sea voyages, you realise that it cannot be depended upon entirely for your regular supply. However, the bioflavonoids (called vitamin P, or rutin, but part of the C complex) in citrus fruits, peppers and buckwheat are vital for the health of capillaries and blood vessels, and fruit fibre is similarly important for the health of the digestive system.

Lime juice was used by the Navy in the eighteenth century to prevent scurvy (a vitamin C deficiency that causes bleeding gums, lost teeth, internal haemorrhages and eventual death). That is how we got our 'limey' nickname.

Herbal teas for Pisces

Parsley. Chamomile or valerian to soothe and restore. Blackcurrant leaf or rosemary for water retention. Evening Peace, China Light and Morning Starter by Jill Davies. Rosehip. Limeflower and Peppermint by London Herb and Spice Company, for the effects of overindulgence.

13

Individual sun sign approaches to headaches, colds and flu

Headaches

(If headaches persist, consult a registered osteopath to ensure that there is no spinal distortion. Cranial manipulation can also be of enormous benefit.)

Aries With Aries (ruler of the head), headaches can be the result of a total physical malaise. Probably you will have been driving yourself for days if not weeks, ignoring stress symptoms and snatching junk food snacks. For you, headaches are a warning sign and not to be taken lightly. You must rest, onerous though you find such a necessity. Find somewhere peaceful and lie down. Clench each muscle, starting with the feet, hold for a few seconds and then relax, breathing deeply and evenly. A relaxation tape would be invaluable to you, to help you in crossing that boundary of tension that motivates you. Contrary to your inner beliefs, the world won't fall apart without you, and learning how to practise total relaxation regularly will keep you as free of headaches as possible. You will probably dismiss yoga and autohypnosis as quite unnecessary for you, if not outlandish, but as you are reading this, I shall take the opportunity to tell you that either or both of these would help you enormously. As you are one of the longest-lived signs, the quality of your life will become increasingly vital to you, and as you are ahead of most with your beliefs, why not with your own health care?

Taurus With Taurus, headaches are most likely to be brought on by overindulgence and may range from a dull ache to full-blown migraine. If accompanied by faintness, a feeling of weakness, trembling legs, rapid heart beat or dizziness, then they are most probably associated with low blood sugar (hypoglycaemia). Sweet foods and alcohol elevate the blood sugar to astronomical heights and then, as the pancreas struggles to cope with this emergency, insulin is rushed out so fast that blood sugar drops dangerously low. It does not take much common sense to realise that this situation is a stressful one for the body, and what is more, it will happen at least once a day if you insist on indulging in sweets, chocolate (much higher in fat than chips!), high-calorie puddings, cakes, biscuits and drinks. Eventually, you may find yourself with permanent hypoglycaemia, which will drain you of enthusiasm and interest in life. You may be a wonderful cook and wish to entertain regularly, but rich, sweet food that makes a wonderful treat once in a while is devitalising when eaten every day. There is no need for nearly half a pound of sugar in cakes, as some recipes would have us believe! Dried fruit, carrots, dessert apples, maple syrup, unrefined honey or sugar-free fruit juice can provide the sweetening power. Regular consumption of oats and porridge, complex carbohydrates and high-fibre vegetables and fruits is the best defence against rapid alterations in blood-sugar levels, so incorporate them into your diet every day. If headaches and a feeling of depression persist, then it may be due to wheat and dairy products causing an allergic reaction, so it would not harm to exclude these from your diet for two or three weeks to see if your headaches improve. To cope with that shaky, downhearted feeling that low blood sugar brings, take B complex, vitamin C, zinc and a chromium pill, with a protein snack and a drink of soya milk. Rest quietly. Make a note of what you eat at each meal and how you feel three to five hours afterwards, because that is the time when your blood-sugar level will have fallen after eating unsuitable foods. The thyroid is often involved in blood-sugar problems, so get this checked out if symptoms continue. Kelp and vitamin E together are thyroid helpers. Ensure that when you drench yourself in perfumes, as Taureans love to do, you do not inhale the spray; this can cause allergic headaches.

Gemini It is useless telling you Geminis to rest when you have a headache! Your diet may be so poor that you are short of most nutrients and living on your nerves. When you eat, you gulp without chewing and you can have an appetite like the bird that is your symbol. A few mouthfuls of sugary, starchy food, and you are full. So eat the most nourishing food first at mealtimes. Simple head-rolling and neck-stretching exercises can help to prevent the build-up of shoulder tensions that cause your headaches. Lift the shoulders right up to the ears as far as possible, hunch them tightly and then let them drop. Do this a few times each day to keep off the worst tension headaches. There are two acupressure points just behind the ears and these may well be tender to the touch. Gently massage them to keep off the pain, then drop the head forward, roll it slowly, upwards to the left, and let it drop to the front. Repeat to the right. Do this five to six times each side and you may find your headache is already fading. Vitamin C to protect your lungs, B complex, and a daily multivitamin are very important for Gemini. If you can persuade yourself to stop long enough to have a regular full-body massage, this will keep some of the tension at bay. Overstimulating mental activities late in the evening should be avoided if possible as this overexcites the brain. Too much brainwork and not enough fresh air frequently contribute to Geminian headaches. As nerviness is likely to be behind the pain, take a soothing luke-warm bath for thirty to fifty minutes, dry yourself gently and rest in a warm room.

Cancer Cancerian headaches are often caused by worry about loved ones and simple relaxation therapy can be invaluable here. Dancing to music is soothing, and water therapies can be helpful. Too much caffeine and meat is damaging to this sign (caffeine and saturated fats are implicated in cystic breast disease) for they will block the system. A one-day fruit and water fast once a fortnight will help to clear out toxins and keep weight down. Too many toxins = too many headaches. Six glasses of mineral water daily will also help. Hypnotic therapy will greatly help the compulsive worry that can cause Cancerians so much anguish. Ensure that your pillow is supporting your head and neck properly at night. Do not eat between meals, and never eat big suppers late at night – even if you feel that you need the comfort of food. There are some very pleasant herbal teas that will help you to relax at bedtime.

Leo The build-up of poisons caused by too much overeating and alcohol is as likely to give Leos a headache as it will Taureans. Nor will you Leos be eager to change your dietary habits, being positive that you are right in everything you do. Changes have to come from inside you, and these can be slow or absent. Complete rest in a quiet, comfortable room is vital when Sun-ruled people are feeling drained of energy. If it's a sunny room, then even better. Bright yellows, golds and topaz colours around you will help you to recover. Keep a headache file that contains colour photographs of all those whom you hold most dear and look through this when a headache strikes. Read favourite poetry and listen to a familiar soothing piece of music – and don't be too proud to admit there is something wrong with you!

Virgo Health-conscious as you are, Virgo, you are also one of the tensest signs and like to have everything done yesterday. Perfection can be your downfall, a fact of which you can be surprisingly unaware. Does it matter if things get a little untidy and all your colours don't blend, for once? Unfortunately, for Virgoans it does – and the very fact that you can't be perfect twenty-four hours a day and create a perfect world around you is enough to give you the most draining tension headaches. Small, regular meals are as important to this sign as a high-fibre diet and complex carbohydrates. Deep-breathing exercises, music and flowers will help to elevate your moods, and an ioniser will keep the air fresh and pure if you are working on computers, which is quite likely. B complex is important for your nervous system, and a good intake of fibre will prevent your lower digestive system going into spasm. Keep herbal tranquillisers to hand for those days when your stomach ties itself in knots, for the next stage is a splitting headache. The lukewarm bath described for Gemini will soothe Virgoan nerviness.

Libra Beautiful music, the scent of flowers, a beloved pet to hold, a romantic message from a lover – any of these can chase away the Libran headache.

Feeling neglected, unloved or forgotten can give this sign some profound headaches. You need to feel needed. You need to have your faith in human nature reinforced at regular intervals. Strife and argument will give you headaches. The regular use of aromatherapy will bring about a pleasant sensation of wellbeing, and many of the Eastern methods of relaxation are made for you. Like Cancerians, you may need the comfort of food late at night, but this can create a build-up of toxins which will poison the system. Relaxing herbal teas can be very soothing, while chocolate and cocoa are frequently a cause of headaches. Like Taurus, you are fond of perfumes, but make sure that you do not inhale the spray when applying these, as sensitivity headaches may arise as a result.

Scorpio Scorpions have a tough constitution that can resist virtually anything. If you get a headache, then it is a signal that you absolutely must take it easy for a while. Put aside your wish to rule the world from behind the scenes, and commune with Nature and the harmony of the Earth. Walk by the sea and listen to the rhythmic sound of the waves; let the gentle rain caress your face; learn a new water-borne sport that will completely remove your thoughts from worldly concerns for a few days. Remember that other people must have their turn now and again – it can't always be you. Realising this will alone prevent quite a few Scorpio headaches. Regular deep breathing will help you to cope with the build-up of intolerable tensions.

Sagittarius Liverishness may be at the root of the Sagittarian headache. Meditation will bear fruit here. Sagittarian Winston Churchill's catnaps are famous, but it is not generally known that he was actually meditating, not napping. Such a force of fiery energy drives this sign that lying down to rest is something you would not dream of doing. Somehow, meditation does not seem like rest to you, so you can accept it more readily. Select a piece of suitable music and play this each time to hasten the transition to the state of meditation. Remind yourself that you will be a stronger and more able person for these regular sessions. Six glasses of mineral water daily will help your liver to sweep out toxins, and a regular one-day fruit and water fast will help to prevent their build-up. Dandelion coffee tones liver and kidneys and should be a regular item in your diet.

Capricorn The Capricorn headache is likely to be accompanied by a feeling of dispirited gloom or even a black-cloud depression. The Bach flower remedies can be useful here (see appendix). You may feel out of sorts and totally frustrated, as if every one of your desires is eluding you. Early life for Capricorns can be one long headache as you strive to achieve yet find your ambitions annoyingly evasive. Anything that helps you enjoy life more will cut down on your headaches. Life is too short to drown yourself in gloom and negativity. You may well feel that sport is of no interest, but the general toning-up that you will gain from some regular activity is invaluable. Exercise can help to lift depression, as scientific research has proven.

Aquarius Aquarians don't often get headaches and can be quite alarmed if one appears. A brisk walk in the fresh air is one of the best remedies for you. Storms that create the Uranus-ruled lightning can bring on a headache, and lying down in a quiet room is helpful here. Massaging the acupressure points behind the ears, a cold compress on the forehead, or gentle scalp massage will speed recovery. A regular time alone is essential for Aquarians.

Pisces   When bodily fluids are choked or blocked by emotional upset or physical trauma, you Pisceans can suffer debilitating headaches. Regular swimming will help to keep you streamlined, as will a regular walk by the sea or a river. With your unevenness of purpose, you may start a crash diet and then feel so miserable and unhappy that you gorge on all the wrong foods. (See Taurus for the dangers of hypoglycaemia.) Spiritual belief of some sort is vital to you, and without this you can feel so anchorless that you eat all the wrong foods and drink too much alcohol, not caring what damage you do to a body that you feel has little value. A course in self-assertion would bear fruit. Watching fish swimming, or painting beautiful pictures, can be very restorative for this sign.

Colds and Flu

Aries   Ariens won't stop because of a streaming cold, but as this is a Fire sign, you may develop a high temperature as a result of a virus infection. Too much Fire needs a little water, and this remedy should help: wrap up well and sit in a very warm room. Put the feet in a bowl of water as hot as you can tolerate, and allow the body to sweat heavily. The treatment can be repeated, but restrict the sweating after the first time. Taking vitamin C daily (at least 1g) will help to keep infections at bay. Always take it with water, as tea, coffee and alcohol destroy it. Increase the dosage if you have been in contact with a bug, or if you have to work in a smoky atmosphere. Alternately, as soon as symptoms appear, take a long dose of strenuous exercise, but not to the point of exhaustion or aching muscles. If symptoms persist or worsen, try the above hydro-therapy treatment. Drink as much water as you can stomach.

Taurus Taureans love to have the opportunity to be pampered. Take plenty of vitamin C and freshly squeezed lemons with unrefined honey. Tuck yourself into bed with a hot-water bottle and some pretty tissues. Eat light, nourishing foods until you feel better. Avoid foods and drinks that affect your blood sugar and put you under greater stress: tea, coffee, sugar, refined foods, sweets, alcohol, undiluted fruit juices. You might find sugary treats a great psychological comfort, but they destroy the body, cell by cell. An old remedy for sore throats is charcoal, and charcoal pills can be sucked, or dissolved in the mouth, to soothe a painful throat.

Gemini Because you neglect yourself and devour so much junky food, you may find that your colds and flu are monumental. Your body will leap at such infections to rid itself of the build-up of toxins caused by your unhealthy life style, and you will sneeze and blow nonstop! This is not to be discouraged, and you should never be tempted to take drugs that suppress cold symptoms. Let it all out, and be thankful that there's an escape for so much accumulated poison. Afterwards, build up your strength with multivitamins, vitamin C, B complex, small, nourishing meals, fresh fruit and vegetables, and garlic. To stimulate a poor appetite after flu, take three garlic perles three times daily. If a chest infection is involved, take a gulp of mineral water each time that you cough, for this is the best cough cure. If the congestion is very bad, try a hot foot bath, a hot drink, swaddle yourself in blankets and apply a hot fomentation to the chest for a few minutes. It is important to do this in a draught-free room and to rest afterwards, warmly wrapped. If you are getting too many colds, try this breathing exercise: the moment that you feel symptoms beginning, inhale, expanding the lungs as far as possible, and count to twenty while holding the breath. Do not rush the counting. Breathe out as far as possible, then hold while counting slowly to ten. Repeat the exercise, breathing in and out at least forty times. This will tone up the Gemini lungs and improve their circulation.

Cancer See the recommendations for Taurus, and drink lots of mineral or spring water, low-sodium preferably, e.g. Volvic. Swimming is one of the best ways of building stamina and resistance to disease, and is well suited to your sign – but do ensure that you don't get chilled. The old-fashioned stodgy puddings that you adore do nothing to build up vigour. Eat lots of fresh fruit and red and yellow vegetables and take extra vitamin C.

Leo A Leo with a cold or flu is a sorry sight, but you love to be waited on and pampered with hot-water bottles and fruit drinks. If you insist on soldiering on, remind yourself that you are spreading germs to others and this is hardly an heroic way of behaving. Remember that sugar and sweets weaken the immune system, so do not indulge in sweetened cough lozenges and mixtures. Use a herbal and garlic cough medicine such as Liqufruta, and inhale Olbas oil. You will recover quicker in a sunny room.

Virgo Even the perfect Virgoan can catch a bug, and it can be your body's way of demanding a rest. You should increase your dosage of vitamin C and garlic, drink plenty of mineral water and take a pile of books and magazines to bed. Your powers of recovery are swift and you can bounce back after the worst bouts of illness, just as the mercury in a thermometer leaps upwards. This may be the only time that you can be persuaded to rest, so for this reason alone your body may decide to contract more colds than your healthy life style would suggest. You can't fight fate. Your body knows best, so give way to it. A hot-water gargle will soothe a painful throat. Try this every three hours, for at least five minutes.

Libra A lot has been said about lazy Librans, but usually you loathe anything that keeps you from your many interests. Flowers in your room will have more of a restorative effect than anyone would think possible, and aromatherapy treatment was made for you. If your symptoms are not too severe, take a bath with those oils recommended for chills and colds (e.g. wintergreen), keep warm and rest in bed afterwards with a bowl of fresh fruit to hand. It is important to drink plenty of (sugar-free) fluids when ill, to keep your kidneys flushing. Tea and coffee are diuretics and should be avoided in excess. If cystitis or a chill on the kidneys develops, avoid all colas, chocolate, peppers, spices, alcohol, tea, coffee, sugar, aspirin, baking soda and refined foods; keep the feet, hands and back warm; and drink copious amounts of water. It is more important to drink than to eat during the acute phase.

Scorpio The drive to keep working while sneezing is powerful and you may refuse outright to rest. This is a fixed sign, and your views are strong. However, it is ruthless to spread your germs amongst the innocent, and others may become far more seriously ill with the bug than you are. Your enjoyment of work may be so powerful that you resist all the bugs that come your way, but as with hard-working Virgo, sometimes your body knows best, and you must listen to it and rest. Take vitamin C and plenty of fresh fruit. Now could be the time to try some of those exotic fruits you've always fancied. Take a little of your paperwork to bed with you if you must, because boredom would only make you feel unutterably miserable.

Sagittarius Sagittarians are usually forward-thinking and interested in the latest remedies. A Fire sign like Aries, you too may develop high temperatures, and naturopathic remedies are best for these. Drink plenty of mineral water to keep the liver flushing out poisons, with vitamin C to invigorate. For fevers, try the hot foot bath mentioned under Aries. Your restlessness may drive you outdoors before your symptoms have properly abated, but it is better not to endure any extreme changes of temperature at this time, or a chest infection may result.

Capricorn Another fixed sign, it has been said that Capricorns would carry on working through an earthquake! All that your loved ones may be able to do is make sure that you eat well and take your vitamins, unless you are stubbornly convinced that health care is total nonsense. As with Virgo and Scorpio, your body will now and again insist that you rest, and it is far wiser to listen to it, or you will be setting in motion far more trouble for yourself. Keep warm, sip herbal teas such as peppermint and rosehip, inhale Olbas oil and rub a little on your chest to ease breathing. Prevention is better than cure, so remember that next time you refuse your vitamins.

Aquarius This is a sign that revels in all the latest treatments – the more unusual, the better. You will enjoy trying out the old-fashioned naturopathic remedies just because they now seem so new and novel after years of being pushed aside by allopathic medicines. You may like this one: at the first signs of a cold, take a bath as hot as you can bear, while ensuring that your upper half doesn't get chilled. After about fifteen minutes, step out of the bath, wrap yourself in a sheet and lie in bed with the covers piled on top to facilitate sweating. This will help the circulation and speed the exit of poisons. (It is most important not to get chilled between bathroom and bed.) Sip diluted fruit juices and take extra vitamin C, zinc and garlic.

Pisces Pisceans need to tone up the lymphatic system when suffering from colds and 'flu. One-quarter to one-third of the blood is lymph, and hydrotherapy treatments will support and tone this system that is essential to the body's defences against disease. Your room should not be too hot or airless (but beware of draughts). Fruits and vegetables keep the body alkaline, which nourishes the protective white blood cells. (Acid foods such as tea, coffee, meat, dairy products, nicotine, alcohol, refined sugars and flours, all make the body acid, which inhibits the white blood cells.) Do not take aspirin or any suppressant drugs as these inhibit the body's natural reactions to illness, and Pisceans need to keep their treatments as near to Nature as possible. Do not sleep with the bedcovers over the face. One simple hydrotherapy treatment for this sign is as follows: as soon as you feel a cold coming on, immerse feet in hot water, adding more hot water to keep the temperature constant for twenty minutes. Afterwards, immerse feet in running cold water, dry thoroughly and put on warm socks and slippers, or rest in bed. Massaging the feet with peppermint oil will be soothing, but do not attempt a reflexology treatment while ill – wait until you are better.

14

Individual sun signs approaches to insomnia and overweight

To Insomnia

Aries You need so little rest that your normal night's sleep would be considered galloping insomnia by anyone else! Usually you only need five or six hours and never have trouble dropping off. In the event of excessive stress, however, when your mind is racing, you may well be restless. In this case, as you do not like any elaborate medications, two herbal tranquillisers such as Quiet Life or Kalms and a milky drink should do the trick. For bedtime reading you will enjoy the life stories of other fearless and pioneering Ariens such as Lady Jane Digby, Houdini, William Booth or Clara Barton, founder of the American Red Cross.

Taurus Indigestion or heartburn after a heavy evening meal is the most likely reason for your lying awake. It is advisable not to eat after dinner time, as food will be improperly digested and this will worsen your weight problem, too. Peppermint tea is soothing for indigestion, or a little milk, sipped slowly. Commercial indigestion remedies often contain aluminium and are not recommended, for aluminium damages the brain. Tea and coffee in the evenings will also overstimulate you mentally – and keep your kidneys working overtime. If your sleeplessness is caused by worry due to some unsettling change in your regular routine, Jamaica dogwood may well be the herb that will help you, but this must be prescribed by a herbalist. A good book has always worked wonders for Taureans, so keep one by the bedside – a richly coloured art or nature book or a passionate romantic novel.

Gemini What is insomnia to those who prefer to stay awake half the night? If you have to make an early start next day, avoid all stimulants the night before, read a nonfiction book (preferably a technical one) and take two or three herbal relaxant pills such as Quiet Life or Kalms with a milky drink. Evening Peace by Jill Davies is one of the more pleasant 'nightcap' herbal teas.

Cancer Worry is probably the root cause of your insomnia, and a course of herbal relaxant pills such as Quiet Life or Kalms will help overall. Autohypnosis is invaluable to fend off obsessive worry, and once learned, this can have you asleep in minutes. A hop pillow would also be of value. Family sagas are the perfect bedtime reading for you.

Leo Soothing music, a dull book and a milky drink should be all that is needed for the cat-napping Lion. However, if sleeplessness is the result of shock, consult a herbalist for a restorative tincture. Books on royalty and celebrities of stage and screen are the ideal bedtime reading for you, for success stories hearten you.

Virgo Herbal sleeping pills are invaluable for your overactive brain. A hot milky drink and tryptophan will be beneficial. Autohypnosis will help to get you across that great yawning divide created by your

high-speed brain. Most likely, tension is the cause –
so take a course of herbal tranquillisers, as suggested
for Cancer. Primrose tea is recommended for tense,
restless Virgoans, and, as you love to be close to
Nature, a hop or herb pillow to make your dreams
sweet-scented. If nerves are ragged, take a course of
calcium and magnesium (these work together): 1000
mg calcium and 200–500 mg magnesium daily. At
bedtime, select a beautiful picture book such as the
Country Diary of an Edwardian Lady, or John Clare's
nature poems. If persistent stomach discomfort is
causing your sleeplessness, try excluding cow's milk
from your diet for two weeks, as this may be causing
an allergic reaction.

Libra   A romantic novel, a hot milky drink or chamomile tea, a comfortable bed with fresh, lacy sheets
and pillowcases, often have a wonderful effect on a
restless Libran. In the event of needing something
stronger, you will enjoy trying out the different herbs
recommended for sleeplessness, such as hops,
valerian, limeflower or chamomile. A herbalist will
be able to suggest a suitable tincture. There are some
very attractive hop pillows available at herb and
health shops these days. An art book, such as one
on the pre-Raphaelites, is the perfect bedtime reading
for the male Libran (who may well secretly read
romance, too).

Scorpio   Like Aries, you need very little sleep; but
if intolerable tension is getting you down, then try
primrose tea, and substitute herbal teas for tea and
coffee. Chamomile is pleasant and soothing, and hop
tea is a very old remedy for taut nervous systems. A
course of Quiet Life or Kalms may be necessary if
you have been overdoing things again. You too will

enjoy a good romantic read at bedtime, or something with a metaphysical theme.

Sagittarius You may well deny that you have sleeping problems, and shut yourself up in your room and suffer rather than reveal what you consider to be a weakness, but any of the soothing herbs already mentioned will work for you quite quickly. A good brisk walk in the evening will make you pleasantly tired, and if you have been playing a sport, wind down properly and finish with some cooling-off exercises. A strong saga encompassing worldwide travel and powerful interrelationships is your most suitable bedtime reading.

Capricorn It may be a shortage of calcium here, so take a few raisins, a hot milky drink with honey, and a calcium and magnesium pill late in the evening. Make sure that there are plenty of dark green, leafy vegetables and oranges in your diet. You too like to suffer in silence and hate to take pills, but surely you can see how impractical that is? If it is depression that is keeping you awake, with black thoughts filling your mind, try the Bach remedy mustard, or consult a herbalist about lily of the valley tea. You read extensively and love the printed word, but make sure that your bedtime book is not too exciting or violent. Corporate intrigue or more spiritual themes should suit you.

Aquarius You are usually an excellent sleeper, but tryptophan can be invaluable if you hit a bad patch brought on by stress or your freedom being threatened in some way. Try a course of autohypnosis, or practise deep, slow breathing, counting to five while breathing in and five while breathing out, concentrating on the movement of your stomach muscles as

you breathe. Increase the calcium in your diet and
make sure that you are getting enough exercise. A
fantasy or science fiction novel is your perfect
bedtime reading. If you prefer nonfiction, try something on the latest research into a branch of the
metaphysical.

Pisces You are one of the great worriers of the
zodiac, fearful of what may happen to you, to your
loved ones, to the girl next door, to . . . and so on.
Meditation will level out this anxiety, and the gentle,
peace-loving religions of the East will appeal. Select
a mantra such as 'Love' or 'Peace' and you will feel
that you are contributing to the improvement of the
world as you relax your body. Avoid sleeping drugs
and alcohol, which inevitably get Pisceans into diffi-
culties, and try one of the pleasant sleep-inducing
teas such as Evening Peace by Jill Davies. A reflective
evening walk by water will help to prepare you for
sleep. A tape of the sound of the sea, the waves
swishing and swirling, will free you of tensions. It is
important that your bedtime reading is pleasant and
beautiful; a gentle, humorous romantic novel would
be ideal, or poetry on the beauties of Nature.

Overweight

Aries The true Arien is always enviably slim, lithe
and, if anything, a little underweight.

Taurus Your sweet tooth has led you into many
weighty problems. You love rich foods, sugary
puddings, expensive wines. You feel that life is not
worth living unless you can indulge yourself. French
cuisine is your downfall. It can be a long, painful
road to sensible eating, even though you are basically

one of the most sensible signs of the zodiac. A one-day grape and mineral water fast is an easy way to start your diet. You can tell yourself that it's only one day, after all. Next morning, you may well have lost two to three pounds, and that will hearten you for the next step. Change cream for Greek yoghourt (not the strained variety, that is comparatively high-calorie); change butter for grapeseed oil and low-fat margarines (avoiding hydrogenated fat, which is unhealthy).

In the first days it's permissible to keep some low-calorie drinks handy to console yourself with, but eventually it would be better if you changed to unsweetened fruit juices diluted half and half with mineral water. The new Perrier with lime and lemon is delicious, but as Perrier is high in salt, do not drink it if you have a water-retention problem.

Herbs and garlic can give you that comforting taste of French cuisine without the fattening elements. Pizza herbs can be added to casseroles and omelettes, not just pizzas. A high-fibre intake will make you feel full and free your body of accumulated toxins. You can eat a huge dish of crunchy raw vegetables and consume very few calories. The trouble with high-calorie food is that it is often soft textured and slips down fast in large quantities, adding rolls of fat to the body.

Puréed celery, cucumber and tomatoes, with pizza herbs and garlic added in generous quantities, can make a delicious soup with very few calories. If you must have something extra with it, try rice cakes; there are quite a few different varieties and these too are low-calorie if you don't drown them in butter. Unpolished, organically grown rice is an excellent, nourishing diet food. It has few calories, is high fibre and can be prepared in many different ways. Eat it with beans to increase its protein content.

Here is a suggested slimming menu:

For breakfast, a plateful of one variety of fruit. To drink, peppermint tea, or decaffeinated tea with skimmed milk. (Tea should never be taken without milk as milk neutralises the tannin.) Stick to one type of fruit. Take 1 g of vitamin C and a multivitamin.

For lunch, rice cooked in bouillon with garlic and pizza herbs, a large green salad, your choice of sugar-free beans, fresh mint if you have it, and tomatoes. 1 g of vitamin C and B complex tablet.

For dinner, fish baked with pizza herbs and garlic or spring onion, tomatoes and courgettes. Side salad of scrubbed raw vegetables. Baked apple with plain live yoghourt topping and six raisins or a flaking of almonds.

For snacks: crudités, one apple, Chinese lettuce leaves filled with slivers of low-fat cheese, popcorn cooked in as little oil as possible and eaten as it comes, without butter or sugar – quite a lot can be eaten without adding noticeable calories, and this will satisfy the urge to munch on something.

To drink: herbal teas such as chamomile, mint, peppermint and rose; the Secret Garden and Jill Davies' range are imaginative and interesting. Decaffeinated tea or coffee with the day's allowance of half a pint of skimmed milk. One or two glasses of unsweetened fruit juice diluted half and half with water. Six to eight glasses of mineral water. On waking: hot water with a squeeze of lemon (a Victorian beauty tip).

Keith Timson's low-calorie mayonnaise: 4 oz (120 g) of grapeseed or olive oil; one large carton of live plain yoghourt (if it has been pasteurised then it isn't live); 4 oz (120 g) low-calorie mayonnaise or salad cream. Reduce the amount of oil for an even lower calorie dressing. Mint or garlic crystals can be added for extra tang.

General tips: if you have a particular addiction, then there is a possibility that your body may have built up a sensitivity to this food or drink. You may feel quite desperate if you have to exclude it from your diet. In this case, a herbalist or naturopath will be able to help you. Acupuncture has been of great help to addicts, not only of the more dangerous drugs but also of nicotine and even chocolate. The important thing is to keep your blood-sugar level on an even keel. Missing meals, drinking sugary tea and eating sweets, bread and jam, cakes or biscuits will all cause your blood sugar to rise and then fall dramatically, at which point you will have such a craving for something sweet that you will be unable to eat sensibly. Oats and oat bran, porridge, soya, wholegrains, protein, fresh fruit and vegetables (raw or very lightly cooked and with the water then added to soups or casseroles), B complex and brewer's yeast will help to keep your blood sugar flowing evenly.

Gemini The true Gemini never has a weight problem. If anything, you may be a little underweight. If so, anything that helps you to relax will be of benefit. Never eat when tired or cross, chew slowly and rest after meals. Take B complex every day. Bananas, raw honey and wholemeal bread snacks will help you to add a pound or two, and make sure that you have your daily quota of fresh fruit and vegetables, for you need the minerals in these.

Cancer Cancerians love good plain cooking but eat too much of it. You yearn for dumplings, suet puddings, traditional cakes and meat and two veg. The first step is to throw out all your refined foods and replace them with plain live yoghourt, wholegrain flour and cereals, wheatgerm, unsweetened muesli (commercial brands are high in sugar and salt), organically grown brown rice, wholemeal pasta, sugar-free baked beans, fresh fruit and vegetables. Try this low-calorie but traditional-style casserole: slice courgettes, tomatoes, apples, onions and low-fat cheese and put in a casserole dish, layer upon layer, with a final layer of cheese on top. Flavour with herbs to taste, and garlic (start with just a little if not used to it and remind yourself how healthy it is: it protects your heart and arteries, and is a natural antiseptic and antibiotic). Bake for 45 minutes in a moderate oven. You can soon lose your waistline if you don't take care of your diet. Keep a picture of Cancerians Cyril Smith or Henry VIII on your fridge to remind you of the penalties for overeating and lack of exercise, and think of Britain's heaviest living man, Arthur Armitage of West Yorkshire. He's a Cancerian.

Leo   You do everything on a large scale, and that can include monumental indulgences at mealtimes. You may be a lazy Lion, but most Leos are usually quite active, with strong enthusiasms which don't allow them to stagnate. When dieting, choose sunny-coloured foods that will cheer your spirit: carrots and low-fat cheeses, yellow tomatoes, russet apples, yellow capsicums; add garlic, saffron or golden curry powder to your cooked dishes; flavour with mustard, paprika or cinnamon. Eat a mango for a treat when you deserve a reward. The regular one-day fruit fast is very restorative for you. Drink Perrier flavoured with limes.

Virgo   You are usually slim and lithe, but the Earth Mother Virgoans may put on a little weight after having children (although Sophia Loren is a prime example of the Earth Mother Virgoan and she has kept her enviable contours). You are probably already on a healthy diet; but if not, to get things moving try the one-day grape fast with mineral water. Extend it to two days if you can stay quietly at home. Massage and aromatherapy will help you to shed the fat quickly. You may have been too busy for exercise. Make time for walking briskly or bicycling. Tension can ruin your digestion, so eat slowly, chew well and rest after meals. Never eat when rushed or upset.

Libra Another of the overindulgers of the zodiac, born with a sweet tooth, you are a connoisseur of all the richest, sweetest dishes and wines. Even though you know all the bad news about sugar and refined foods, you may be unable to re-educate that sweet tooth. Acupuncture could help you here – and also the oats, porridge and unsweetened muesli diet mentioned for Taurus, to keep your blood sugar level. For snacks, try popcorn without the butter and sugar: sprinkle it with ginger or cinnamon. Keep a dish of crudités in the fridge. Munch on an apple. Think of the bounty of Mother Nature: sweetened, processed foods are as far removed from Nature's offerings as it is possible to be. Eat only foods which you can mentally trace right back to their *natural* origins. The large majority of packet foods are Foods from the Dead Zone (see appendix). If you falter, remind yourself of Jon Brower Minnoch, the heaviest man in medical history (100 (600 kilos) stone at his peak!). He was a Libran.

Scorpio Always energetic, small-boned and slim, you don't know what obesity is. If you are on the cusp with Libra, it may be another matter. In that case, if you are overweight, read the recommendations for Libra and Taurus.

Sagittarius You may overindulge, but you are one of the most active signs so matters may balance out. If they don't, try the one-day fruit fast and take a few hours out from the clamouring world. Cut out butter, white bread, sugar, sauces, pickles and jams, and those few extra pounds will soon roll off. Increasing your hours of sport wouldn't do you half so much good as cutting out these unhealthy foods plus alcohol.

Capricorn Usually you are a past master or mistress at cutting out foods that you know are bad for you. There is none of the compulsive attraction for sweet dishes that Libra and Taurus suffer. If you are hooked on a dish it is likely to be a plain, solid one, like bread and cheese. Wholemeal bread is fine, but cut down on the cheese and substitute low-fat varieties. Drink more mineral water and try out some herbal teas. Tea, coffee and alcohol are very acid-forming and will encourage a tendency to arthritis and aches and pains in the vulnerable Capricorn bones. You rarely put on excess weight.

Aquarius Also slim and active, you may well have a crutch to keep you going – and if this is smoking, then buy in some sunflower seeds and eat them every time you feel like a cigarette. Keep blood sugar level by eating small, regular, protein-packed meals. Have oats or porridge for breakfast, flavoured with cinnamon, ginger, or raw, unrefined honey. If you put on a few pounds after cutting out the cigarettes, this will go in a few months when your body has balanced itself again. You need plenty of fresh fruit and vegetables to keep your circulation healthy.

Pisces Like fish, Pisceans can be eel-slim or whale-like. Daniel Lambert, one of the world's heaviest men, was a Piscean. He also liked swimming in the local river. Swimming is one of the best activities for this sign, but drifting in the water won't get rid of that fat. You must swim hard until you feel toned up. Being waterborne also gives those Pisces feet a rest. Bicycling will do this, too. You may have tried many crash or fad diets in the past and stuck to them for three hours or even four, so what you need is a regular sensible diet that is easy to maintain and doesn't require much thinking about. First, eat more fish. Try out herbs and spices and garlic in place of sauces and pickles, which are high in sugar. Eat more jacket potatoes, and instead of butter or cheese on them (which also makes them indigestible), add minced garlic, low-fat sauce (e.g. Keith Timson's Salad Dressing), or a sprinkling of chopped herbs. Throw out all your refined foods and commercial cereals. Get in the habit of buying everything sugar and additive free. This means reading a few labels until you accustom yourself to the contents. You may find reading the chemical contents of your favourite foods shocks you so much that you will continue to take an interest. Keep plenty of fresh fruit and vegetables in the house. Snack on sugar-free, butter-free, home-popped popcorn. Try the Japanese kelp dishes, an acquired taste but rich in nourishment that will help you stay free of excess fluids. Foods rich in potassium will do the same, and these include melon, vegetables, unrefined grains, fresh fruit and fruit juices (always to be diluted half and half with water). Morton's Lite salt is high in potassium, as are some other salt substitutes; generally, salt is to be avoided as it causes water retention to which Pisceans are prone. Volvic mineral water is low in sodium (salt).

15

Getting back in touch with Nature

> Do not worry about what the future may
> bring, but strive to become firm and
> clear within. For it is not how fate
> fashions it, but how you come to terms
> with fate that will bring your life's
> happiness.
>
> *Georg Wilhelm Friedrich Hegel*

Mother nature's bounty

Astrology centres round the rhythms of Nature and
the ever flowing seasons. Winter is the time for
Ceres-Demeter to mourn her lost child, and thus the
three winter sun signs – Capricorn, Aquarius and
Pisces – may suffer more depressions than other
signs. Spring is the time for the blissful reunion of
Mother Nature and her beloved daughter Persephone, when the burgeoning plants and trees
proclaim their happiness together, bringing lightness
of heart or a closeness to the Earth to the three spring
sun signs – Aries, Taurus and Gemini. Summer is
the ripeness of this love, the re-establishment of the
maturity of the mother/daughter relationship and the
three summer sun signs – Cancer, Leo and Virgo –
are the maternal triplicity, the ones who care so
deeply for children and those in need. Autumn
brings the first signs of the coming of winter and
the loss it will engender, when Libra, Scorpio and
Sagittarius, the reproductive trinity, as if aware of

the barrenness to come, are more fertile and produce more children.

Mother Nature – Ceres, Demeter, Cybele, Rhea, Gaia, Isis, as she is variously called – was once the most honoured and worshipped of the deities. People were sensible then – they knew that they depended on the Earth for everything and that it was wrong to take without being grateful, without giving something in return. People were fully conscious of their unity with the Earth. They knew without being told that if they raped Mother Nature then they would pay a high price. Today, we see the results of this rape: the denatured soil, the pesticides in earth, river and stream, the destruction of the cycles of Nature, butterflies almost wiped out, the ozone layer split open, fruit painted with chemicals to make it look glossy, natural foods discarded in favour of complex chemical formulae. Foods from the Dead Zone are just that: they are winter's foods, foods that should never have existed because there were not the sunshine, sweet fresh air and earthy minerals to create them. Mother Nature was not given the chance to smile on them, for they were created in test tubes in laboratories, by men who have tried to take the place of the Harvest Queen. As if they could!

Astrology is all about returning to the ageless rhythm of the seasons, to the realisation that people have different qualities because they are born at different times of the year. Every twenty-four hours, we see a mirror of the year: night is winter, morning is spring, afternoon is summer and evening is autumn. The great cycle of the seasons is repeated daily, and it is possible that if you were born at night you have some of the basic qualities of the winter signs; born in the morning, some of the basic qualities of the spring signs; born in the afternoon, some of the basic qualities of the summer signs; and born in the evening, some of the basic qualities of the autumn signs.

The tree, once the sacred asherah of the Great Goddess religion, its roots in Mother Earth, its trunk rising to the heavens into which its branches reach, has been threatened for many years. The equatorial forests are being decimated, and this is drastically changing the Earth's climate. Trees have been cut down to provide more grazing land for cattle that will end up as fast-food burgers. In place of Demeter we have Mammon. Naturally, Earth will rebel against such crimes. I have heard so many people say that trees mean nothing, that they have no purpose – yet they exude the oxygen that we need for life. Without them, we would be dead. If it were a case for a burger or for suffocation, which would you choose?

We need to respect Nature, to cherish everything that she brings us, to stop force-feeding cattle, to stop producing animals on a massive scale and keeping them in inhumane conditions, fattening them up with antibiotics and hormones. The pig was once sacred to the Goddess, too – and look how it is treated now: forced to stand up in a narrow cage for fear that it might roll onto its young. What human mother would like to give birth and suckle her young standing up, and then stay standing up until her young were weaned?

The cow, too, was sacred to the Goddess, and now her young are torn away from her so that humans can have her milk. Cows do not give milk unless they have borne a calf, but they are not allowed to roam the fields with their little ones. The calves are taken away and the cows are hooked onto milk machines.

Crows were sacred to the Goddess, too. They are raucous, rowdy glorious birds that are now shot as vermin. Owls that were her sacred bird, symbol of her wisdom, are at risk. Snakes, her symbol of eternal life and the continuation of the seasons, the closeness to the Earth and its secrets, are the cause of wide-scale phobia . . . or their richly complex meaning stripped down to one of the most basic sexuality. Her dove was adopted by the Christian Church, so that at least is safe!

When did you last think of the source of the food you are eating? Do you rush your meals, gulping and swallowing as if your life depends on it? The truth is that your life depends on your eating quietly, chewing thoroughly and keeping to foods that come from natural, unadulterated sources. It is better that food is allowed to grow as wildly as possible, for it is the very wildness that maintains its nourishment, the naturalness and vigour of the Earth. It's more difficult the natural way, of course, and at times may seem like a constant battle with Nature, instead of a cooperation, but many have succeeded beyond all their dreams. Read about Findhorn, where huge vegetables are grown in the barest soil, with faith and communion with Nature. Every plant, tree and bush has its own Nature spirit, and every piece of land over which you have jurisdiction, whether it be field or farmland, garden or window box, should have an area left wild for Nature to flourish in her own way. Leave that section to grow as wild and uncultivated as possible, and do not invade it. As time passes, you will feel a build-up of power there, a sensation of strength, a force. At night, you may find that area in your garden almost too forbidding to approach. Nature's forces are powerful ones; it is the force field of Nature that you sense: an ancient, pagan vigour.

The body considers cooked food alien and sets up barriers against it, so before a cooked meal, eat something raw first – a piece of fruit, sprouted seeds or raw vegetable – to smooth the passage of your food. Do not use aluminium cooking pans as this metal is incriminated in Alzheimer's disease, the degenerative disease of the brain that causes advanced senility. For the same reason, do not use water that has been standing in a pan or kettle for any length of time. Mineral and spring water is best; it comes from the rich, restorative womb of Mother Earth. Every morning, whether your cold-water pipes are lead or copper, run the water before usage, as the water that has been standing will be contaminated. Copper destroys vitamin C in the system, and lead causes brain and kidney damage. For the same reason, do not use copper cooking utensils (too much copper can cause depression, anger, hostility and tenseness).

I do not advocate cooking by microwave, either, for three reasons. Firstly, it encourages people to eat cooked meals instead of raw vegetables, salads and fruits. Secondly, there has been some rather worrying research involving food cooked in this way. It may affect the white blood cells, the ones that are vital to the immune system in fending off disease and illness. Thirdly, it adds yet more radiation to the home, and there is already more than enough with televisions, computers, electrical equipment, word processors, radios and natural radiation itself. Home should be a haven, not a place where we are bombarded with radiation.

Eating in a quiet place is essential. Picnics, despite their drawbacks – insects, wet grass, spiders and plastic-flavored drinks – remain perennially popular for the simple reason that it feels good to eat out in the open, close to the Earth, perhaps with a pretty stream dancing nearby and birdsong all around. You can smell the rich green of the grass and the clover, breathe sweet fresh air, see wildlife running free.

Eat outside as often as possible. There is nothing so beneficial.

When you eat Nature's fast food, such as an apple, hold it in your hand, look at it, see it properly for the first time since you were a child, think of the tree that it grew on and the rich Earth beneath, and understand that you are a part of that rich Earth.

When stressed, sit quietly and sip mineral water and think of the life-giving heart of the Earth where that water came from, bestowing its mineral richness for you alone. Earth cares for you as your mother, if you will only let her, and the Earth Spirit (who has many different names) is a nurturing, healing force – but only if you are in tune with her. Two thousand years of Christianity, and the emphasis on a male-dominated religion has almost eradicated our intimacy with Earth and Nature, the feminine heart of our world and of us. How many people thank God for the harvest when it is Mother Nature, Demeter, the Harvest Queen, who is the bountiful One? The balance of Nature is no myth; it is of paramount importance, but it is seriously endangered on our planet today. If you are out of tune with Nature, then you are out of tune with your own health and happiness, with your very purpose for being here. Return to natural fruit and vegetable growing in your garden. Offer thanks when plants flourish. You may feel odd, or even ridiculous doing this at first, but that only shows how far away you have come from Nature. If you realise that all living things possess a spirit, then it won't seem so ridiculous to talk to your plants; you will also come to realise the sense of listening to what they say in return. For example, when you are more in tune with Nature, you will be able to walk into a room where there are plants desperate for water or light, and sense their distress.

Food grown naturally, with Nature on your side,

not against you, is the healthiest food – and its balance will ensure your own balance of health.

'If you want to be of the light, then you must eat the light', is a strong argument in favour of the vegetarian diet. Plants are full of light; they need it to grow. When you eat them, you are filled with that light. Meat, artificially raised and the result of the slaughter of animals, is dark food, devoid of light. Meat-eating can make you grouchy because it encourages a highly acid system. This causes other acid cravings such as those for tobacco, alcohol, sugar, tea and coffee. Alternately, plant-eating will make you sunny-natured, for it keeps your system alkaline, as it should be for health.

When you eat in the vegetarian style then you are in control of your diet. When you eat a largely meat or processed diet, it is in control of you. The vegetarian way of eating needs to be planned care- fully. Various foods contain different amino acids and have to be eaten together at each meal so that you get your protein complete. Beans on toast is a popular meal that provides a complete protein. Indian dishes such as vegetable curry and chapattis, or pilau, also provide complete proteins. Your dishes can be complemented as follows:

Mix sunflower seeds with peanuts. Peas or beans with corn. Wholegrain wheat with peas or beans, or soya and sesame seeds. Rice with peas or beans, and low-fat cheese, or sesame, soybeans, tofu or soy sauce. Peanut butter with wholemeal bread. Wheatgerm with yoghourt. Tofu can be added to vegetables and puddings. Soya protein comes in some delicious varieties these days, not like the early days of sawdust soya!

Proteins that are complete in themselves include eggs, cheese, black walnuts, soya and milk, and any of these added to a vegetarian meal will increase its nourishment. Make sure that your eggs are from free-range hens. Happy hens lay happy eggs. Also, when raised naturally, hens go off lay at certain times. This is Nature's way of allowing them to recoup their energies. Battery hens are never given this chance. The eggs are flogged from them, figuratively speaking. Stressed, tormented hens produce stressed eggs that are less nourishing.

It is important that raw beans are boiled for ten minutes before being cooked further, for this breaks down the toxins within them that can cause an upset stomach. Soak them overnight beforehand to speed the cooking and to help reduce gas after they have been eaten. Bringing them to the boil and pouring off the water three times will help even more.

If you are changing to a vegetarian-style diet, don't rush matters. Do it gradually, giving your digestive system time to adapt. Pregnancy is not the time to decide to change to vegetarianism, as mother and baby may go short of nutrients during the adaptation period. There are many excellent books with recipes that produce meals with a balanced, complete protein content. The body can store vitamin B12 for some years, but you must be aware that vegetarians can run short, especially if your stores are low when you stop eating meat. Eating live plain yoghourt will help to supply this vitamin. (Pasteurised yoghourt is not live.) Vegetarians may also run short of lysine, and foods rich in this amino acid include:

Cottage cheese, milk, eggs, fish, liver, lamb, beef, ham, peanuts, pumpkin seeds, soybeans, soy flour, almonds, peas, bean-sprouts, cauliflower, strawberries.

Lysine also fights herpes very effectively, and taking 500 g daily, plus ensuring that you eat plenty of the above foods, may keep those painful break-outs at bay.

A mindless consumption of food can cause more damage than temporarily going a little short of the correct proteins as you get your dishes balanced out. You will by now be thinking about food seriously, maybe for the first time in your life. It can be argued that the body knows best – and indeed it does, if given the chance. But it has no chance if you have introduced it early to sugar and junk foods. Like your soul, your body can be corrupted. It will soon learn to crave sugar, chocolate, nicotine, alcohol, tea and coffee, and you will be helpless to control this.

On the old-fashioned diet of wholegrains and wheatgerm, garden-grown vegetables and corn, cracked wheat (bulgar), fresh milk and cheeses, and locally caught fresh fish, the body flourished. A treat was a treat. One ice cream a week, if a child was lucky. Some only got ice cream on holiday – if they had a holiday. It was a real thrill to have a fizzy drink.

Many children now breakfast on cola and dough-nuts or sugary cereals made with refined flour – if they breakfast at all. The result is a dramatic blood-sugar drop at elevenses, when they will feel so savagely hungry that they rush for sweets, chocolates and soft drinks. By lunchtime, they are quite crazily hungry and stock up with fatty foods and sugary puddings, being just too ravenous to eat salads and vegetables. If this continues for too long, the pancreas becomes so flustered and exhausted that a child may be on the first steps to diabetes. Mentally, they suffer too. 'Crazily' hungry becomes 'crazily' behaved. They lose control; their mood-swings increase; they feel too tired even to think straight; sudden surges of aggression and violence pour out of them. They lose track of the difference between right and wrong. (In cities, this problem is exacer-bated by the lead in petrol. In America, lead petrol has been banned for some time and the improvements are now visible.)

This is the root cause of the behaviour problem, and it all begins with the bottle-fed baby being filled with cow's milk and white sugar. Calves grow at a rapid rate and become enormous by comparison with the growth rate and size of the human infant. We are forcing our children into obesity, and giving them a sweet tooth before they even have any teeth!

A story featured in the press some time ago concerned a race-horse that was given a Mars bar as a treat. One Mars bar, that was all, but it registered in the horse's blood at drug level! Horses are far bigger and sturdier than we are, yet humans are accustomed to eating such sweets every day. My children composed a verse when they were small: 'A Mars a day helps your teeth to decay.' When they were tired of singing that, they sang: 'A Mars a day helps your body rot away.'

Restful nights

Chocolate may be one of the major causes of snoring. It is a food highly dense in sugars, milk and, sometimes, harmful additives. The body has a struggle to metabolise it, and after all that work, very little nourishment is the reward – and possibly allergy or migraine. Dairy products feature largely in allergies; so do wheat and caffeine. Add to an already concentrated sweet the density of refined sugar that is required to sweeten it, and you have a cocktail of ingredients that sensitise the body. I know someone who needs to eat only one chocolate bar to snore extensively at night for perhaps three or more nights. Normally, he is on a healthy diet and takes plenty of exercise and is fitter than most. This snoring effect is not the result of a poisoned system; it is a genuine allergic reaction. The body forms excessive mucus in its struggle to evict the toxic dose (for the same reason that mucus forms during a cold, to evict the bacteria) and snoring, snuffles, a frog in the throat or a feeling of being 'blocked up' can be the result. In ayurvedic medicine, milk has long been recognised as a mucus former.

If snoring is your problem, try the exclusion diet on these lines: for one week, cut out all sugar, chocolate and sweets – especially brightly coloured sweets. You may find that this causes an immediate improvement. It is a small price to pay for a saved marriage! If this does not work (and if your body is sluggish and out of condition then it might not), cut out all dairy products for one week . . . plus the chocolate, sugar and sweets.

By the end of the second week, you should be feeling much fitter, even if the snoring has not improved dramatically. If you feel fitter, you will have more energy, move faster, sleep better and have more enthusiasm for life. All this can result just from excluding all forms of sugar and chocolate!

At the end of this period, if you wish to test the veracity of this recommendation, eat some chocolate. Watch to see what reaction you have. You may have snuffles, a runny nose, a clogged feeling, an immediate headache. You may feel tired a little later. You may crave an immediate dose of caffeine or nicotine.

Snorers should never eat late in the evening and they should not eat mucus-forming foods for dinner. These include all acid foods such as meat, tea, coffee, alcohol and dairy products. Try instead a big mixed salad (salad and vegetables – bar tomatoes – are alkaline) with fish or cottage cheese. Eat fresh fruit for pudding and drink diluted fruit juice and herbal teas during the evening. It is worth it to find out that you need not snore like a thunder machine all night. With men, alcohol is often the worst offender: highly acid, it causes a great accumulation of mucus. Sleep is deeper because of the affects of intoxication. Snorers are often heavy, almost comatose sleepers anyway and rarely hear their own sound effects, all of which points to the artificially deepened sleep of an allergic reaction. When snoring hour after hour, the body is under great stress and there is the risk of oxygen shortage to the brain. It is incriminated in high blood pressure and many diseases.

Gradually easing your body away from the acid diet of tea, coffee, alcohol, sugared foods, confectionery and an excess of meat and dairy products, and onto a more alkaline diet of salads, fruits and vegetables, will not only help the snoring but also improve your general health considerably.

Happy days

If you feel that you cannot wake up without tea or coffee or a cigarette, if you crave meat at mealtimes, then your body is highly acid. In the early days of Earth population, Stone Age man had to work hard to catch his meat. Sometimes he would fail, but there would always be a chase involved, and long waits between meat meals. Today, meat is thrust at us from all sides. It is no longer the Sunday treat that it once was. We have bacon for breakfast, burgers, sausages or chops for lunch, perhaps more burgers for dinner – or steak or minced meat. In America, the birthplace of fast food (which is what you would expect of a country with Gemini rising!) children may eat sugary doughnuts, coke or jam waffles for breakfast, burgers and white rolls for lunch, and frankfurters for dinner.

In Britain, children often miss breakfast or have sweets or fizzy drinks or crisps on the way to school, then have chips for lunch and more sweets or cola, with a white-bread sandwich for tea and meat and potatoes for dinner. Whenever adults or children are tested for vitamin and mineral deficiencies, they are frequently found to be short of something vitally important, such as iron or folic acid.

Restless, impatient, short-tempered children grow up into aggressive, self-centred teenagers who snack on chocolate bars and crisps. This food is easily obtained. It costs them no effort. To their adulterated tastes, it is delicious. But every time they eat sugar, they are robbing their systems of calcium – a great tranquilliser as well as a bone and teeth builder. They are also being deprived of the B complex vitamins because the body uses up these in its efforts to digest refined sugar. Vitamin C is devoured by the body as it fights nicotine, caffeine and air pollutants. Shortage of vitamin C means that iron is not properly assimilated from food. (Taking vitamin C with iron-rich food can double the amount of iron absorbed.) Too many soft drinks also strip the body of calcium and vitamin C. Refined foods are stripped of zinc, which is vital for a happy mind, and the result in severe cases is a loss of appetite (anorexia is its most extreme form), loss of interest in sex, depression, slow wound-healing and infertility. The Pill robs women of their zinc. Alcohol, cigarettes and cortisone interfere with the body's absorption of this mineral.

The best sources of zinc are seafoods (particularly oysters, long renowned as virility food!), herrings, liver, mushrooms, shrimps, crabs, wheatgerm, brewer's yeast, meat, onions, sardines, wholemeal bread, milk, eggs, peas, carrots and potatoes. If you take a zinc supplement, make sure that it is amino-acid chelated to help full absorption and utilisation.

Unleavened bread contains phytate, which blocks the absorption of zinc. Once bread has risen, the phytate is inactivated. Stretch marks may be a sign of zinc deficiency (not just on the stomach but on thighs, hips, breasts or shoulders). Acne may be another sign. To grow strong and healthy, hair and nails need zinc. White spots on the nails can be a symptom of zinc shortage.

Teenage girls may experience delayed menstruation or irregular periods, while boys may not mature sexually as they should. Aching joints or 'growing pains' can also be an indication. Insufficient zinc may cause lack of growth. Loss of sense of taste or smell can be another symptom. Zinc can also help with the irritated nasal passages of allergy, so it may well be useful in the fight against snoring. Diabetics have no zinc in their pancreas. Listlessness, weariness, disinterest in food and loss of hair are other signs.

It is wiser to avoid processed and frozen foods and alcohol if you want to keep your zinc levels high. Most of the zinc is removed during the refining process of grains and sugar, and children who live on snacks, junk food, sweets and sweetened fizzy drinks will most certainly be short of this vital mineral. They will also be moody and easily tired, lack enthusiasm, and find stressful occasions such as exams deeply depressing. If you have depressions, moodiness, a feeling that life is one long struggle, if you never know that jolt of pure happiness, then you may well have been zinc deficient since childhood. Eat as many of the zinc-rich foods as possible, abandon sugary foods and fizzy drinks, check that the canned food you eat is not sweetened (much of it is – even vegetables); cut out sugar in your tea and coffee. Fruit (although vitally necessary for other nutrients) does not contain much zinc, so have a zinc-rich pudding after each meal. Bread pudding made with grapeseed oil instead of butter, wholemeal bread instead of white, and sugarless jam or marmalade to flavour, sweetened with maple syrup, plus milk, is a zinc-rich dish. Or have seeds for your pudding, or add seeds to rice pudding and salads for a nutty taste.

Happiness begins with the right balanced diet, and for this you need as many different foods as possible each day. Compulsions for refined food (for example, gorging on ice cream, especially late at night) will cause malnutrition eventually, and the first symptoms of this may well be a feeling of vulnerability, a gloomy mood, a negative outlook. Exhaustion and a sensation of being weighted down are other early signs. How can you enjoy happiness if you are so out of touch with Nature, for this you are bound to be if your diet is wrong?

You may never have been in a health food shop, but when you do go in, you will see that the predominant colour on the shelves is brown – not white, as in supermarkets. Brown is the colour of healthy food: golden-brown wheatgerm, wholemeal flour, wholemeal semolina, wholegrain rice, bulgar wheat, wholemeal pasta, nuts and zinc-rich seeds. The most nourishing foods are the colour of the Earth. The most damaging foods are the colour of purity: white sugar, white flour, white salt, white saturated fat, dairy cream, heroin and cocaine. . . .

The simple rules for happiness are as follows:

Eat a natural, unadulterated diet with wholegrains, unprocessed foods, fresh fruits and vegetables. When you eat, think of the source of the food. Eat an apple and look at it carefully. Examine its colour and texture and then relish its taste. Think of the tree from which it came and the roots of that tree burrowing deep into the Earth to fill the apple with nourishment just for you.

If you live in a flat or room, get out into the open air regularly. Walk on grass bare-footed and feel the Earth's power beneath your feet. Smell the flowers and the greenery. Think of what happens beneath the Earth's surface: the powerhouse that is thronging there at all times.

Find someone to care for. Give money to charity – it doesn't have to be a fortune; even a small amount will feed and protect the health of a Third World child. Commit yourself to helping others in some way on a regular basis. You may find this difficult at first; you may feel shy and awkward and dread being misunderstood, but the important thing is that you help others. This should be your major aim, so keep this in mind and it will help you to overcome any problems along the way. It does not matter if the recipients of your care are abusive in return, or ungrateful or disinterested; or even if they accuse you of ulterior motives or self-interest.

When you feel angry, hostile or vengeful, remember that these emotions rebound on you, doing more harm to you than they ever do to the object of your hostility. They are like black-magic spells and curses – and these always rebound on those who have sent them. That is the law of karma: every action has a reaction. Practise loving thy neighbour and loving thy workmate – not in the physical sense, of course, and never for self-reward, but in the purest spiritual sense. Cast your bread on the waters, but never ever think of what it will bring you in return. To be truly happy, you must forget about self and all those sharp, clamouring needs and desires that drive you.

Every time that you do something for your own benefit, also do something for someone else's.

If you are doing things for money and to help your chances of promotion, things that you know are wrong, give them up. If you are hurting others in the pursuit of your own gains, then you know deep inside that this is wrong. You know that it will rebound on you eventually, however clever and sharp and safe you think you are now.

If you are unemployed, feeling full of despair and caught in a terrible trap of frustration and desperation, if you are bitter and blaming the world, the government, religious groups, ethnic groups, life, your wife, etc, etc, think again. Every new generation has problems to cope with, to learn from. Remember, that is why we are here. Life is not meant to be all roses and sunbeams; that is too easy. Character and spiritual strength are choked before they can bloom, in an easy, comfortable life. Whatever you may think you want, your spirit is struggling, deep down inside, to be good and strong so that you can help others. It needs hurdles and setbacks. From these, you will grow strong. It may sound old-fashioned to say that problems are a test of faith, but that is what they are. When you are envious, sour, bitter, when you feel that your luck will never change, you must throw out these negative emotions, and have faith that all will turn out right in the end.

Finally, and certainly not least of all, adapt your mental attitude. You can change that, but you can't change the world – and you have no right to expect those around you to change to suit you. From the moment you take your first breath, life is all about adapting: to the air you breathe, the food you receive from your mother, the fear of darkness, the feeling of loneliness and terror that grips you when your mother doesn't respond instantly to your cries. Then its painful falls when you try to walk, and that big dog that looks so frightening and makes you shrink back, the cars that roar all too close when you're trying to cross the road, the rough tumble of playgroup, the first days at school, school tests, making and losing friends, the ordeal of exams and adolescence, first crushes, first real love. . . . Why should your adult life be any different? What is amazing is that it does get easier – but only if you learn your lessons along the way. There are some elderly people who are still as petulant and egocentric as small children: you must find compassion for them, and for the wild ones, the angry, ill-mannered ones, the ones who have never been loved or protected, even the violent ones. Compassion is what makes human beings mature; it is one of the most tender and consoling emotions. Forgive where you can, and always forget that slight, that injury. I do not mean be weak or allow others to escape the prices they should pay for serious wrongdoings, for that would encourage them to stay immature. You may forgive; you may forget; but they must pay the allotted price.

None of us are forced into this world. We want to come. If it helps you to understand, think of Earth as a school, a place where you are always learning. Some of the lessons are difficult, some are really tough, some are almost soul-destroying. You may suffer, lose loved ones, face despair; you may loathe your parents, your siblings, your workmates, but if you keep in mind the fact that you yourself chose this life, these parents, this situation that you are in now – and that you chose it for your own soul's good – then it will help to ease your distress. When you blame others for your situation, you are in fact blaming yourself for choosing it.

Between lives, when we are choosing when and where we shall be born again, we keep in mind the lessons we have learned and the ones that we have failed, and we select a situation that will teach us what we need to know. We want to hone our spirits and improve ourselves. When in spirit form, we long for the right lessons, however arduous and painful they might be.

Yet when we get here and have to face the truth of what we have chosen, it can be tough. Things are too bad, too upsetting, too disturbing. Surely no loving God would ever foist these disasters on His people? He doesn't. We choose them ourselves, with a great deal more wisdom than our physical bodies would give us credit for. If we have been evil or cruel or irresponsible in a former life, then we want to pay the price now and improve ourselves. We want to be better. If we fail because the path we have chosen is too hard or life itself too stringent, if we fall back and make mistakes again, then we will have another chance. This is not the only life – how foolish and wasteful if it were. Mother Earth wastes nothing: her plants and trees, her flowers and fruits return again and again to blossom and burgeon, and winter to them is like death is to us: yet we return again, out of the darkness, into a new body, a new life, just as they do. If we have forgotten this passage of the seasons, this ancient, timeless rhythm that affects us as much as it does the Earth herself, then it is because we are so out of touch with Nature.

I believe that this is the true meaning behind those words, 'The spirit is willing but the flesh is weak.' Having deliberately chosen the drawbacks we must face, we arrive in our new settings only to find that we sometimes can't face what we have chosen. Our spirits want to learn and improve and become purer, but how oppressive it is when worldly matters weigh down on us, when there is an easy path to take instead of a more difficult but better one.

It is pleasant to believe that we have a right to happiness, but why should this be so? What if we spread unhappiness in our previous life, what if we were downright nasty, spiteful and destructive? Should we be rewarded in this life? Wouldn't that be unfair? This may be the life that we have chosen to put matters right, so maybe it can't be smiles and sunshine all the time. One thing is sure: the sooner that you set about making recompense, the sooner contentment will come to you.

It is all very well believing in the Christian teaching that all men (not to mention women and children!) are equal, and in an ideal world this would be so; but we do not live in an ideal world. It is just as misleading to say that all people should be happy, or rich, or handsome. In the teachings of the Eastern religions, particularly Hinduism, everyone is considered to be at a different level of karmic evolution, so there is no envy or sourness. What good would it do to someone to be rich, handsome and talented, with everything placed at their feet, if they are in their present life to learn what it feels like to be poor, or helpless, or unemployed?

Unfortunately, although wonderful in concept, man's (and I mean man's) interpretation of Christianity has caused far more havoc and anguish than would have existed without it. This notion that all men are equal has given thousands of people the motivation to demand, steal or take what they feel should be theirs. Why should there be beggars in the streets when all men are equal? Why, indeed?

Each new life that we begin gives us a new birthchart, maybe a different gender. Sometimes we have subconscious memories of a previous gender, and this may govern our behaviour. We may think and feel like a woman but have a man's body, or vice versa. Easy to see how this could happen to anyone and how, when translated into our present day life, the sort of problems it brings.

Something that happened to us in a previous life

may have been truly unforgettable – some sort of violence, or a difficult or violent death. The memory is always there in the subconscious and hypnotherapy, in the hands of a registered and skilled hypnotherapist, can help us to deal with this painful memory, which may be affecting us still. This is not, however, a task for a new or untrained therapist, or for someone wishing to practise on you. The results of reliving a painful former life experience can be traumatic if you are not in skilled hands.

Keep in mind that we are on the brink of a far better age than we can ever anticipate now with all the problems that beset us. It will be a happier world with brotherhood and sisterhood surrounding us. The coming Aquarian age will be all about the unity, humanity and benevolence of humankind. People will come to understand that this difficult Christian notion of all men being equal has misled us into many detrimental patterns of behaviour. Also to be clarified will be the equally difficult notion over which scholars and clerics have racked their brains for thousands of years: how can a loving God let us suffer?

We are not punished, or allowed to suffer by a loving God. We choose our lives and the way that we must live them, just as we choose a course of study at school, for good or for bad. It is all in our own hands. Let us make good use of our time on this Earth by living in tune with Nature, and be thankful for the opportunity.

When the light gets brighter, as it is doing now, the shadows increase in darkness. That is why it may appear at the moment as if evil is winning. It isn't – and it never will. Keep that in mind at all times, and love will be the victor.

Appendix

Acid/alkaline foods

Acid-forming foods   Sugar, salt, meat, cheese, gum, chocolate, dairy products, tea, coffee, alcohol, tobacco, refined carbohydrates, pepper, curries, soft drinks, fried foods, highly spiced and seasoned dishes, aspirin, white rice, refined pasta, sausages, pies, pasties, cakes, etc., made with white sugar and white flour, tomatoes, starchy refined foods, eggs, fish, pickles, sauces, mayonnaise and salad cream, milk, pâté, jams and preserves. Mixing refined starchy foods with proteins, e.g. meat pies, ham and beef burgers with rolls, steak and kidney pudding, and egg custard, results in the protein being digested first and the starch fermenting in the stomach and causing hyperacidity.

Alkaline-forming   foods   Vegetables   (especially green ones), fruits (citrus fruits, although acid before being eaten, become alkaline in the stomach within a few minutes), unsweetened fruit juices (always dilute, half and half with water), cabbage juice, alfalfa, salad greens and vegetables, herbs, sprouting seeds.

The Bach flower remedies

Dr Bach was so totally in touch with Mother Nature that he could select flowers, prepare them and prescribe them for various physical and psychological problems. To the orthodox mind, this may seem bizarre or improbable, but the fact is that the Bach remedies work. Dr Bach was no unqualified charlatan. He was a Licentiate of the Royal College of Physicians, a Member of the Royal College of Surgeons, a Bachelor of Medicine and of Surgery, and he held a Diploma of Public Health. I have used his remedies personally over the years, for myself and my family, and have never been disappointed with the results. They will work even when the recipient does not know they are being given them (a student who was suffering from exam stress but hates taking vitamins was given the appropriate remedy in fruit juice and an improvement was obvious within a few days). There are remedies for anguish and depression and unbearable disappointment, but it would not be correct to say that one remedy alone will suit each sun sign, or that Dr Bach advocated any connection between his 'Twelve Healers', as he called his original twelve remedies, and the twelve signs of the zodiac. The Bach Centre states categorically that this is not so. Individual character and personality have to be taken into account when selecting a Bach remedy or remedies. One of the very helpful Bach booklets is *Questions and Answers* by J. Ramsell and N. Murray, which will clarify the basic principles behind the flower remedies and tell you more about them. *The Twelve Healers* by Dr Bach will tell you all you need to know about making your selection. In this booklet, he says that no science or knowledge is necessary, apart from the methods he describes, for prescribing this simple treatment. Few other remedies are so brilliantly in tune with Nature herself, few other remedies a more generous gift from the Earth Mother to us, her children.

The address of the Bach Centre is:
Bach Flower Remedies Ltd, Dr E. Bach Centre, Mount Vernon, Sotwell, Wallingford, Oxfordshire OX10 0PZ

The Bach supplier in the USA and Canada is:
Ellon (Bach USA) Inc; P.O. Box 320, Woodmere, New York 11598, USA. (Tel. 516 593 2206)

The Bach suppliers in Australia are:
Pharmaceutical Plant Company, P.O. Box 68, Bayswater, Vic. 3153, Australia. (Tel. (03) 762 8577/8522) AND Martin and Pleasance Wholesale Pty. Ltd; P.O. Box 4, Collingwood, Vic. 3066, Australia. (Tel. 419 9733)

The Bach Centre will happily answer any questions you need to ask, and will supply you with their booklets and the appropriate remedies. Health shops also stock the remedies, but do not use them before reading about selecting a remedy to suit your particular temperament. The Centre will also provide a list of distributors elsewhere in other countries.

Foods from the dead zone

Any of the following foods may be implicated in simple functional low-blood sugar problems (hypoglycaemia), the symptoms of which can include tiredness, a feeling of being drained of energy, moodiness, weakness, headaches, depression, black moods and a feeling of futility, anxiety, depression, tension, light-headedness, unexplained hunger, unexplained outbursts, overweight, lack of concentration and insomnia. (This is not a complete list of possible symptoms.)

To avoid White sugar, aptly called 'pure, white and

deadly' by Professor John Yudkin, is one of man's cruellest tricks on humankind. Nature provides sweetening in crude form, deep in the heart of the thickest fibres. Sugar cane looks like bamboo in its natural form; to get at the sugar in it, one needs to bite and suck and chew, and even this effort delivers very little at one attempt. Beet sugar, too, comes in a highly fibrous casing. Like tea, sugar was once available only to the rich who could afford it. Since about 1850, when the duties on sugar were dropped, it has become more widely available, and in this century, we have been force-fed refined sugar in canned foods and sauces, packet and processed food, cakes, scones, buns, biscuits and soft drinks, ice cream, packet puddings, confectionery and sugar-cured tobacco, to name but a few of the ways it reaches us. Refined sugar is filling in that it causes a rise in the level of blood sugar, so a soft drink, chocolate, sweets, or sugary tea or coffee – none of which have any important nutritional value – fill us up and make us feel satisfied. It is like putting water in a car engine. The engine is full, but the contents are useless. It's even worse if sugar is put in an engine – it seizes up completely. That too is the eventual effect of refined sugar on the body.

It is implicated in tooth decay, weakened bones, diabetes, heart disease, blood thickening and clotting, deterioration of the retina, kidneys and eyesight, and, of course, obesity, which leads to other health troubles.

It is no accident that even young children contract diabetes in such large numbers today. Their mothers had a diet high in refined sugar and refined foods, as did their grandmothers (bar the wartime years when sugar was rationed and everyone was on the high-fibre national loaf, a diet which has helped to extend the lives of many). It is now proven beyond doubt that a poor diet can affect a family down to the second or third generation, and I believe that allergic tendencies can also be passed on. White sugar is added to bottle feeds, and breastfeeding has been out of fashion for over two decades: it was thrown out with so many of Mother Nature's wonderful gifts. The culmination of centuries of male-dominated religion has resulted in a situation whereby a woman's body and the nourishment it provides is considered inadequate for the infant's needs – doubt has been cast on a woman's ability to provide: she is no longer the all-nourishing one. Yet cow's milk is for calves and human milk is for human babies.

Dead foods include all refined grains, white flour, rolls, French bread, crackers, cookies, macaroni, waffles, pancakes, doughnuts, bagels, scones, cakes, biscuits, buns, pies and pasties made with white flour, white rice (all the vitamin B is stripped off with the outer casing), white pasta, croissants (high in white flour, white sugar and saturated fat), and bread sticks. White refined grains clog the digestive system, deprive the body of B vitamins, affect the intestinal flora and are implicated in diseases caused by a lack of fibre in the diet. They, like sugar, can be eaten quickly and easily, raising the blood-sugar levels without there having been any lasting nutritional benefit for the body. The eventual result is drastically lowered blood sugar and uncontrollable cravings for more of the same 'poison'. Manufacturers have used the confusion about sugar and blood sugar to promote refined white sugar as an energy-giving, nourishing food. Blood sugar is not in *any* way related to refined white sugar, which provides us with nothing more than high calories that turn to fat, and a temporary energy that is followed by exactly the opposite.

Chocolate packs a punch for the pancreas. High in saturated fat (higher in fat than chips!), high in white sugar, the cocoa powder itself possesses the stimulants theobromine and caffeine. One spoonful of cocoa or drinking chocolate does not seem enough to affect the drinker, but if you or a child are sensitive to cocoa, then it will overstimulate you and possibly cause migraine. It is also very high in calories, and commercial drinking chocolate is high in white sugar. Beware of products in this line which claim to have only natural ingredients but which include white sugar in one of its cunning disguises (variously called sucrose, dextrose, glucose syrup, etc). White sugar is *not* a natural sweetener! Natural sugar is black and tarry and comes in a tough, bamboo-like package. It is called black molasses and is rich in iron.

Rock, that popular seaside favourite, is now advertised as being good for you because all the flavourings are natural, but rock is white sugar, white sugar and yet more white sugar, and it has the same effect on your body as white sugar. So does candy in all its highly seductive colours and shapes. Syrup is not only highly refined but is also high in salt.

Tobacco (often sugar-cured), tea, coffee and cola drinks all have the same effect on the level of blood sugar without affording any vital nutrients. Lucozade, which is sold as a restorative drink for invalids, is high in caffeine and white sugar. Do you want your child to be stimulated into appearing better, to be on a caffeine 'high' instead of recuperating naturally? Freshly squeezed fruit juices are best.

Other Dead Zone foods include all processed and packaged foods – except those prepared without preservatives, sugar, excess refined salt or additives, and which have clearly stated on the label that they are prepared in a natural way from organic products. (Even these should comprise only a certain percentage of the diet: the body needs raw, un-cooked, fresh foods in large quantities.)

Snack foods which have a long list of artificial ingredients, additives, colourings and flavourings are also on the Dead list. What does your stomach make of these? The gastric juices are stimulated, telling the stomach that food is on the way, and then mouthfuls of unidentifiable objects appear, containing strange, unknown, chemically formulated ingredients. Poor stomach. Poor you. Eat only snack foods which are high in fibre, low in salt and sugar, and naturally coloured and flavoured, and always remember that Mother Nature's fast food is best: fruit, seeds and unsalted nuts.

This may appear to be painting a black picture of total deprivation for you, but it is not. If you eat healthily for the majority of the time, there is nothing to prevent you from having the occasional treat. The choice is in your hands. If you want to stay happy, healthy and active, eat wisely for the majority of the time. If you want your children to stay healthy, and raise healthy children, then ensure that they too eat wisely.

Diet for gout and rheumatism

Start your diet with two days on fresh, raw melon and grapes, 5 oz of each at mealtimes. The fruit will provide all the liquid needed. Wash the grapes (and all fruit) thoroughly. Organ meats, fish roes, alcohol, refined sugar and sweets, fried food, condiments, lentils, spinach, asparagus and mushrooms should all be avoided by sufferers from gout and allied conditions as they are high in purine. Uric acid in excess is the problem with gout, and fruits, fruit juices, cherries and berries will help to combat this.

Orotic acid, 4 g daily for six days, will dissolve the painful uric acid crystals and reduce swelling. When suffering an attack, steep the foot in water as hot as you can bear it. As soon as physically possible, make long, daily walks number one on your list of important health factors. Drink as much water as you can stomach every day, to cleanse the system (ten glasses if possible). A swiftly moving circulation will help to protect against gout. Make cherries and cherry juice part of your daily diet as these help the body to cope with uric acid. Take a vitamin B100 tablet three times a day, vitamin C, 2–3 g, and vitamin E, 400 IUs daily. (If you have any heart problems, start on a lower dose of vitamin E and work up gradually to 400 IUs.) Magnesium and phosphorus will also help, as will fortified brewer's yeast and calcium pantothenate.

Make sure that your diet is high in raw and fresh foods, with generous amounts of vegetable fibre – and, if you suffer from constipation, soya bran, too. There is often a history of a sluggish, clogged system with arthritis sufferers, and this is the body's reaction to years of being assaulted by refined foods and toxins. Sensitivity and allergy to certain factors may also be implicated, as well as tea and coffee, alcohol, tobacco, dairy products, chocolate and citrus fruits. It may simply be a matter of finding out the offending factor(s) and eliminating it/them. One person I know was crippled with arthritis and sadly had given up her creative work as she could no longer use her hands. Eventually she discovered that she was allergic to brewer's yeast. She is now restored to full health. (This is a rare allergy, it must be said.) Another, similarly crippled and only able to hobble with a stick, was waiting for a hip-replacement operation. Her mother had become crippled after two such operations; other members of her family had been disabled with arthritic conditions. Her medical advisor said that her problem was hereditary and that she would just have to accept it. After ten days on the antiarthritis diet I gave her, she threw away her stick and is now walking. All her pain has gone.

The Yeast Beast

When antibiotics are taken, they destroy the protective intestinal flora along with the harmful bugs. Vaccination also affects the body in this way, as does immunisation and the contraceptive pill. We are then left in a highly vulnerable state, our immune system weakened, our body's defensive barriers down. The result may be an invasion of candida albicans, a yeast that flourishes at a furious rate if we do not have our own healthy protective intestinal flora to combat it. The Yeast Beast grows as fast as yeast does when fed sugar, and all the foods that we eat which contain sugar give more ammunition to the Beast. This includes fruit and fruit sugar. If you have such symptoms as bloating, unexplained moods or depression, repeated infections, candida (thrush) infections, an unpleasant taste in the mouth, headaches, tiredness and a general feeling of being out of sorts, then you may have candida invasion. Leon Chaitow's book *Candida Albicans* (see book list) explains in detail the symptoms, causes and treatment of candida. At the start of the treatment, even fruit is banned (but only temporarily), and all refined foods, milk, sugar, molasses, maple syrup, maltose, fructose, treacle, honey, biscuits, flour, cakes, jams, preserves, puddings, etc. Yeast-containing or yeast-promoting foods include all fermented products – such as bread, crackers and enriched flours – mushrooms, cheeses, citric acid, truffles, soy sauce, black tea, beer, wines, spirits, ginger ale, ciders, malted products and vinegars. Smoked meats and fish, frankfurters, sausages and corned beef are also to be avoided, as are any nuts not freshly cracked. (Nuts harbour mold.) You may eat wholegrain products if made without yeast or sugar.

Plain live yoghourt will help your protective intestinal flora to rebuild themselves and fight the Yeast Beast, as will acidophilus tablets and powder with bifido. Oat bran fibre should be taken every day to help elimination. Oatmeal porridge is recommended for breakfast, along with mixed, fresh nuts and seeds with wheatgerm. Wholemeal toast, if made without yeast or sugar, is allowed. So are brown rice, oat pancakes, fish, eggs, home-made muesli, rice flakes, oat flakes, millet and natural live yoghourt – these comprise the diet for the first few weeks. Any meat eaten should not contain antibiotics or steroids; Wholefood, in Paddington Street, London (Tel: 01-486 1390) will advise on this. They supply meat that is hormone and antibiotic free from cattle reared to the organic standards set out by the Soil Association. After this initial period of the diet, apple or banana may be included with breakfast, and other fruits may be eaten with the nuts and seeds. Sometimes the treatment must be prolonged to ensure success, but before undergoing this, please consult a registered naturopath, herbalist or nutritionally trained physician.

Some useful addresses

Animal Aid Cosmetics (a natural range of body care, not tested on animals, the profits from which go to the Living Without Cruelty Campaign): mail order from Animal Aid, 7, Castle Street, Tonbridge, Kent TN9 1BH.

Faith Products have been making excellent animal-free products for over a decade, and have now launched the Faith in Nature range, which includes: aloe vera moisturiser, honey and almond moisturiser, essential body oil, seaweed and aloe vera shampoos, and Clear Spring, an ecological laundry detergent. Address: Faith Products Ltd, 52–56 Albion Road, Edinburgh EH7 5QZ, Scotland.

Potter's (Herbal Supplies) Ltd, supply Jill Davies' delicious herbal teas, along with herbal products: Leyland Mill Lane, Wigan, Lancashire, WN1 2SB.

The London Herb and Spice Co. Ltd, Apothecary House, 18 Selsdon Road, South Croydon, Surrey CR2 6PA, supply some of the teas mentioned in the book.

Weleda supply homeopathic remedies and an extensive range of gentle, natural beauty products of a very high standard, without any cruelty to animals. Weleda (UK) Ltd, Heanor Road, Ilkeston, Derbyshire DE7 8DR.

The Body Shop chain sell a wide selection of beauty products and perfumed oils, created without animal testing. The Body Shop's founder, Anita Roddick, is an example of what Librans can do in the beauty world when they set their minds to it.

Hymosa supply a range of animal-free beauty products of a high quality, which are pleasant to use. Hymosa of London, Admail 23, London W3 8XG.

Nature's herbal-care tooth powder, containing 20 herbs,

and with marvellous results for sore and bleeding gums, loosened teeth and gingivitis, can be obtained from: Nature's Ltd, 212 Watford Way, London N2 4UA. (Trial sachet £1.50; 35 g sachet £4.00.) This is highly recommended.

Parodontax toothpaste contains myrrh to toughen gums, sage to deodorise, chamomile to fight inflammation, and sodium bicarbonate to alkalise, plus other healthy ingredients. Available from: Dr Madaus GmbH, D 5 Cologne, West Germany.

Tiki vitamin E oil is highly recommended for dry or sore skin, irritated skin, itchy rashes, strengthening the nails. (For external use.) Available at most health food stores.

Action Against Allergy (AAA), 43 The Downs, London, SW20 8HG. Tel: 01 947 5082 will provide help and information about allergies and their causes. They also sell or loan books on the subject. Please send *large* SAE.

Association of Breast-Feeding Mothers: Peggy Thomas, 131 Mayow Road, Sydenham, London SE26 4HZ. Tel: 01 659 5151, is a counselling and information service about breast-feeding. SAE please.

British Homeopathic Association, 27a Devonshire Street, London W1N 1JR. Tel: 01 629 3205. (Linked with Faculty of Homeopathy.) For a list of NHS general practitioners who practise homeopathic medicine, plus hospitals with a free NHS service. Send SAE.

Acuhealth (UK) Ltd, 31 Ebury Street, London SW1W 0NZ. Tel: 01 730 9511. Acuhealth provide a needle-free, hand-held, battery operated unit called Acuhealth 900, the result of extensive research. Easy to use, quite safe, and containing a comprehensive instruction and treatment manual, the Acuhealth unit will be used for athletes at the 1988 World Olympics. Acupuncture without the puncture!

National Institute of Medical Herbalists, 41 Hatherley Road, Winchester, Hampshire. Tel: 0962 68776 (Linked with School of Herbal Medicine.) Send SAE.

British Naturopathic and Osteopathic Association, 6

Netherhall Gardens, London NW3 5RR. Tel: 01 435 8728. (Linked with British College of Naturopathy and Osteopathy.) Send SAE.

British and European Osteopathic Association, Orient House, 42–45 New Broad Street, London EC2M 1QY. Tel: 01 642 4161.

General Council and Register of Osteopaths, 1–4 Suffolk Street, London SW1Y 4HG. Tel: 01 839 2060

Foresight (Association for the Promotion of Preconceptual Care): Mrs Peter Barnes, The Old Vicarage, Church Lane, Witley, Godalming, Surrey GU8 5PN. Tel: 042 879 4500. (For the promotion of good health in both mother and father before conception to give a trouble-free pregnancy and healthy baby. Informative leaflets, etc, available on request. Please send SAE.)

Migraine Trust, 45 Great Ormond Street, London WC1N 3HD. Tel: 01 278 2676. (SAE for self-help literature)

Herbal suppliers: The Apothecary, Neal's Yard, Monmouth Street, Covent Garden, London, WC2.

Food Watch, High Acre, East Stour, Gillingham, Dorset SP8 5JR, provide (by mail order) basic food requirements minus any additives.

Vitamins and Minerals are supplied by Nature's Best (plus a wide range of extremely informative leaflets on every aspect of nutrition): Nature's Best, 1 Lamberts Road, Tunbridge Wells, Kent TN2 3EQ. Tel: 0892 34143.

Wholefood, 31 Paddington Street, London, supply organically grown fruit and vegetables, cereals and pulses, dairy products and organic wine – plus hormone and antibiotic-free meat from cattle reared to the organic standards set out by the Soil Association. They also have a bookshop.

The Atlanteans is 'a society with a philosophy that offers a sensitive and compassionate approach to life on all levels, based on the principles of love, tolerance and understanding. Within it lies an explanation for man's existence and his role in relation to Nature and all forms of life within the cosmos.' There is a regular newsletter and a book list. Address: The Atlanteans, Runnings Park, Croft Bank, West Malvern, Worcestershire WR14 4BP. Tel: 06845 65253.

The Wrekin Trust is an 'educational charity concerned with the spiritual nature of Man and the Universe. It is not affiliated to any particular doctrine or dogma, does not offer any one way to 'the truth' and helps people find the disciplines most suited to them.' There are regular courses and conferences on the holistic world view, ongoing spiritual training and allied subjects. The Trust has received the Right Livelihood Award (known as the Alternative Nobel prize) given in Stockholm for 'Work forming an essential contribution to making life more whole, healing the planet and uplifting humanity.' Address: The Wrekin Trust, Runnings Park, Croft Bank, West Malvern, Worcestershire WR14 4BP. Tel: 06845 892898.

Recommended reading list

Health

Any books by Leslie Kenton are highly recommended, also those by Leon Chaitow, Geoffrey Cannon, Adelle Davis, Nathan Pritikin, Earl Mindell and Patrick Holford, particularly *Raw Energy* by Leslie Kenton, *Let's Get Well*, and *Let's Have Healthy Children*, by Adelle Davis (if only there weren't the references to animal experiments!). Also, *Better Health Through Natural Healing*, by Ross Trattler.

Alternative Dictionary of Symptoms and Cures, by Dr Caroline M. Shreeve. Century Hutchinson, 1986

Health on Your Plate, by Janet Pleshette. Arrow, 1987 (highly recommended)

The Biogenic Diet, by Leslie Kenton. Century Arrow, 1986 (the natural way to permanent weight loss).

Raw Energy, by Leslie Kenton. Century, 1984 (the eating programme to revitalise you).

The Joy of Beauty by Leslie Kenton. Century/Arrow, 1986 (health and beauty naturally).

The Food Scandal by Caroline Walker and Geoffrey Cannon. Century, 1985.

Let's Get Well by Adelle Davis. Unwin, 1985.

Let's Eat Right to Keep Fit by Adelle Davis. Unwin, 1979.

Better Health Through Natural Healing, by Ross Trattler. Thorsons, 1987 (a marvellous book).

Grandmother's Secrets, by Jean Palaiseul. Penguin, 1983 (herbs and plants).

Nutritional Medicine, by Dr Stephen Davies and Dr Alan Stewart. Pan, 1987 (a guide to drug-free family health).

Pills and You, by Earl Mindell. Arlington Books, 1984 (drugs, what they do to you and how you can protect yourself against their side effects).

The Vitamin Fact Finder, by Carol Hunter. Thorsons, 1987.

More Natural Remedies, by Phylis Austin, A. and C. Thrash, MD. Thrash Publications, Seale, AL 36875, USA (nature cure methods of healing and how to adjust your diet for various complaints – invaluable).

10 Day Clean-Up Plan, by Leslie Kenton. Century Hutchinson, 1986 (clearing your body of toxins).

Everybody's Home Herbal series, e.g. *Herbs for Rheumatism and Arthritis*, by Sarah Beckett. Thorsons, 1985 (Thorsons have a complete list of health and self-help books).

Nature's Way series, especially *Successful Herbal Remedies*, by Nalda Gosling. Thorsons, 1986.

How to Win at Weight Loss, by S. Langer, MD with James F. Scheer. Thorsons, 1987.

Food Combining for Health, by Doris Grant and Jean Joice. Thorsons, 1986 (based on the Hay Diet).

Sugar Blues, by William Dufty. Abacus, 1980 (the true history of sugar).

Dr Atkins' Nutrition Breakthrough, by R. C. Atkins, MD. Bantam, 1982.

Dr Atkins' Super Energy Diet, by R. C. Atkins, MD. Bantam, 1978.

Thorsons New Self-Help series, e.g. *High Blood Pressure*, by Leon Chaitow, 1986, and also any other books by Leon Chaitow, especially *Candida Albicans*, *Your Complete Stress-proofing Programme*, *Your Own Slimming and Health Programme* and *An End to Cancer?*

The Natural Cat, by Norma Eckroate with Anitra Frazier. Thorsons, 1982 (how to care for your cat naturally).

Reflexology, by Anna Kaye and Don C. Matchan. Thornsons, 1982. International Institute of Reflexology, 28 Hollyfield Avenue, London, N11 3BY. (Please send SAE for enquiries about reflexology.)

Complete Guide to Vitamins and Minerals, by L. Mervyn. Thorsons, 1986.

Everybody's Guide to Nature Cure, by Harry Benjamin, ND. Thorsons, 1983. (By the same author: *Better Sight Without Glasses* and *Commonsense Vegetarianism*)

Woman's Change of Life, by L. Mervyn. Thorsons' *Science of Life* series, 1983 (highly recommended).

Raw Juices for Health, by Vivienne Lewis. Thorsons, 1985 (same series).

Liver Ailments and Common Disorders, ed Science of Life Books. Thorsons, 1981 (*Science of Life* series – how to treat with diet).

Nutrition and Vitamin Therapy, by Michael Lesser, MD. Bantam, 1981 (highly recommended).

Yoga for Rejuvenation, by Nergis Dalal. Thorsons, 1984.

Additives Book – What You Need to Know, by Beatrice Trum Hunter. Pivot Original Health Book, Keats Publishing, Connecticut.

Additives – A Shopper's Guide, by Jennifer Pulling. Century Hutchinson, 1985 (additives in popular supermarket foods).

Homoeopathy – A Practical Guide, by Phyllis Speight. Granada, 1979.

Astrology

All books by Liz Greene are most highly recommended and include:

Astrology for Lovers, Saturn – a New Look at an Old Devil, and, for more advanced readers, *The Astrology of Fate*, Unwin, 1985.

The Astrologer's Handbook, by Frances Sakoian and Louis S. Acker. Penguin, 1983 (full of easily accessible information).

Dictionary of Astrology, by Fred Gettings. Routledge and Kegan Paul, 1985.

Jupiter, by Eve Jackson. Aquarian Press, 1986 (an astrologer's guide to the planet Jupiter).

The Planets and Human Behaviour, by Jeff Mayo. L. N. Fowler, 1972.

The Knot of Time, by Lindsay River and Sally Gillespie. The Women's Press, 1987 (the female angle on astrology).

Astrology and Health, by Sheila Geddes. Aquarian Press, 1981.

Astrology: Evolution and Revolution, by Alan Oken. Bantam, 1976.

Contemporary Astrology, by Jerry J. Williams. Shelbourne Press, Nashville, Tennessee, 1977.

Suns and Lovers, by Penny Thornton. Aquarian Press, 1986 (love and relationships – includes birthcharts of the famous).

The Twelve Houses, by Howard Sasportas (with Foreword by Liz Greene). Aquarian Press, 1985 (the twelve houses of the birthchart, their meaning, and the interpretation of planets and signs in these houses, and also the Moon's Nodes and Chiron, the recently discovered planetoid. With example charts).

Arrow Health

] The Gradual Vegetarian	Lisa Tracy	£3.95
] The Alexander Principle	Wilfred Barlow	£2.95
] Health on Your Plate	Janet Pleshette	£4.95
] The Zinc Solution	Professor D. Bryce Smith	£3.50
] Rosemary Conley's Hip and Thigh Diet	Rosemary Conley	£2.50
] Understanding Cystitis	Angela Kilmartin	£3.50
] Goodbye to Arthritis	Patricia Byrivers	£2.95
] Natural Pain Control	Dr Vernon Coleman	£3.50
] The Natural Dentist	Brian Halvorsen	£2.95
] The Biogenic Diet	Leslie Kenton	£3.50
] Ageless Ageing: The Natural Way to Stay Young	Leslie Kenton	£3.95
] Raw Energy	Leslie & Susannah Kenton	£3.50
] No Change	Wendy Cooper	£2.95
] Fat is a Feminist Issue	Susie Orbach	£2.50
] Day Light Robbery	Dr Damien Downing	£3.99

Prices and other details are liable to change

ARROW BOOKS, BOOKSERVICE BY POST, PO BOX 29, DOUGLAS, ISLE OF MAN, BRITISH ISLES

NAME . . . .

ADDRESS . . . .

. . . .

. . . .

Please enclose a cheque or postal order made out to Arrow Books Ltd. for the amount due and allow the following for postage and packing.

U.K. CUSTOMERS: Please allow 22p per book to a maximum of £3.00.

B.F.P.O. & EIRE: Please allow 22p per book to a maximum of £3.00

OVERSEAS CUSTOMERS: Please allow 22p per book.

Whilst every effort is made to keep prices low it is sometimes necessary to increase cover prices at short notice. Arrow Books reserve the right to show new retail prices on covers which may differ from those previously advertised in the text or elsewhere.